The Little ___ ___
Livi.
Life Processes a ___ ing Things in
the Foundation Stage

Written by
Linda Thornton and Pat Brunton

Illustrations by Martha Hardy

Little Books with **BIG**ideas®

The Little Book of Living Things
ISBN 1 905019 12 2

© Featherstone Education Ltd, 2005
Text © Linda Thornton & Pat Brunton, 2005
Illustrations © Martha Hardy, 2005
Cover photo by Sarah Featherstone

Series Editor, Sally Featherstone

First published in the UK, February 2005

'Little Books' is a trade mark of Featherstone Education Ltd

Published in the United Kingdom by
Featherstone Education Ltd
44 - 46 High Street
Husbands Bosworth
Leicestershire
LE17 6LP

Printed in the UK on paper produced in the European Union from managed, sustainable forests

Contents

Introduction

The Little Book of Living Things provides you with a range of ideas and activities to develop children's awareness of the world around them. The themes covered include plants as well as animals, and involve both short and long term investigations. Included throughout the book are some key points and facts to remind you of some of the important concepts which lie behind the organisation and classification of the living world.

These suggestions are intended to help you enjoy your explorations alongside the children and to encourage you to find out more about the fantastic diversity of the natural world in which we live.

Why is the living world such an important area for young children to investigate?

Investigating living things:

? builds on young children's natural curiosity about the world around them, and so provides a powerful stimulus to engage their attention.

? provides many opportunities for first hand learning and investigation.

? encourages children to observe carefully, using all their senses.

? builds children's awareness of the natural world around them and a growing understanding of their responsibilities to other living things.

? helps children to learn more about themselves and how their bodies work.

? develops an understanding of the past, of change over time and longer term investigation and exploration.

? encourages children to be active and to enjoy and appreciate the outdoor environment.

The structure of the book

The Little Book of Living Things is divided into three main sections: Life Processes, Looking After Living Things and Creating Habitats. There is a reference section at the end with further information, resources and books.

Section 1, 'Life Processes' looks at the seven life processes common to all living things, and gives examples, from the animal and plant world, of activities you could do which link specifically to these life processes. These are supported by a section of other ideas entitled 'You could also try...' which suggest related or extension activities which build on the individual themes. Key vocabulary, and links to songs, stories and rhymes are included where appropriate.

Section 2, 'Looking After' provides practical advice on looking after a range of living things in your setting. This will give children the opportunity to study creatures in more depth and to see how they change over time. Ideas for simple investigations are provided, and important safety factors are included (in red type).

Section 3, 'Habitats' looks in a little more detail at some of the different environments which exist around us and the types of plants and animals which live there. This helps children to see the importance of each environment, and to begin to consider their responsibility for respecting and maintaining them. It also provides an opportunity to develop children's understanding of how plants and animals adapt to their environment.

Providing appropriate resources for children to use to explore the environment safely.

These could include:

- 🖐 child sized trowels, buckets, wheelbarrows and spades;
- 🖐 boots and waterproof clothing;
- 🖐 cameras to record findings, events and change over time;
- 🖐 bug viewers, magnifiers, Perry's pooters and transparent plastic boxes for collecting minibeasts;
- 🖐 one or more plastic aquaria to use as a vivarium for keeping snails, stick insects, spiders and caterpillars;
- 🖐 stand magnifiers and good quality drawing materials and paper to encourage children to make close observational drawings;
- 🖐 plastic plant pots, compost, seed trays and planters;
- 🖐 seeds, bulbs, plants and cuttings;
- 🖐 resources for making bird houses, bird baths and bird feeders;
- 🖐 good quality, child sized binoculars;
- 🖐 reference books and sources. Remember your local library will be a good and helpful source.

Promoting a 'living things friendly' environment.

Developing the physical environment of your setting over a period of time encourages a diverse range of living things to inhabit it. You can do this by:

- ● Creating flower and vegetable beds which the children can access easily. These can be use for digging, planting, weeding and harvesting as well as for attracting butterflies and bees.
- ● Leaving an area of the garden as a wild area to encourage wild flowers, insects, beetles and butterflies.
- ● Establishing a low level log pile in a damp shady area to be populated by insects, moss, fungi, lichens, ferns and perhaps frogs, toads and hedgehogs.
- ● Setting up bird feeders, a bird bath and some nesting boxes in different sites around the setting.

The Little Book of Living Things

- Making a compost heap to recycle garden waste, or setting up a composting wormery to process vegetable peelings and scraps from the setting.
- Connecting a rainwater tank to the guttering system to collect rain water for use in the garden in dry weather.
  !Ensure this is a closed system with a well fitting lid which children can't open!

Further information to develop these ideas is provided throughout the book to help you to plan the development of your setting.

The role of the adult

Listening to children

Listening to children involves not just listening to the words that they say, but being aware of the different forms of non-verbal communication they may be using – through gesture, stance or posture – or perhaps the length of time they spend involved in an activity. Listening means being open and receptive to ideas and possibilities and flexible enough to capitalise on opportunities as they arise. It requires an atmosphere in which children feel confident to put forward their ideas without fear of ridicule, or of being told that they are wrong.

Encouraging children to ask questions and have good conversations.

Providing an interesting and ever changing environment for children to explore is an ideal way to develop their natural curiosity, provide opportunities for them to ask questions and talk about the things they have discovered. Spontaneous discoveries – a worm in the soil, a spider's web or a snail under a flower pot are all great starting points for developing questioning skills. Remember the importance of open ended questions like these:

'What do you think the worm might feel like if we carefully pick it up?'
'I wonder if both ends of the worm are the same.'
'How does the spider reach from one place to another when it is making its web?'
'Is it a boy spider or a girl spider?'
'I wonder why the snail is hiding under the pot.' 'How fast do you think it can move?''Do you think it could run away if it was frightened?'
'Have you noticed the lines on the snail's shell, I wonder what they are for?'

Open ended questions encourage children to come up with their own ideas and explanations and can often lead to good suggestions for investigations which you and the children could carry out together.

Using the expression 'What do you think' shows that you value all children's opinions and is a useful way of encouraging the less confident children in your setting to put forward their ideas.

When you are having a conversation with a group of children remember the importance of showing that you value all the different ideas and theories that they come up with, not just those that are considered to be 'scientifically correct'. Children's ideas and theories are based on the many different experiences that they have had and represent their way of making sense of the world. Using these ideas as starting points for further investigation and exploration provides an ideal way of developing children's understanding and experience as well as their confidence and independence.

Don't worry if you don't know the answers!

Developing children's skills, dispositions and knowledge

Skills and dispositions
Investigating and exploring the living world, finding out how our bodies work and learning how to take care of living things provides many opportunities to develop young children's skills and dispositions.

These include the social skills of:
> cooperation;
> following instructions;
> understanding rules and
> personal safety.

Practical skills of:

    close observation;
    using all the senses;
    manual dexterity;
    hand eye coordination;
    measuring and counting.

Communication skills including:

    speaking;
    listening;
    discussing;
    recording.

Reasoning and thinking skills including:

    questioning;
    speculating and hypothesising;
    noticing similarities and differences;
    problem solving.

The activities outlined in this book are also designed to encourage the **dispositions** of:

    curiosity;
    empathy;
    open mindedness;
    a willingness to put forward ideas.

Knowledge

The purpose of this book is to provide practical information to help you develop an awareness, understanding and appreciation of living things among the children you work with and care for.

A wide range of reference books and resources is available to help you extend your own knowledge and understanding, and many of these can be used with the children. These are listed in the reference section at the end of the book.

Just in case a child asks you if a spider is an insect, or if all worms are the same, this diagram explains (for you!) the grouping and classification of plants and animals.

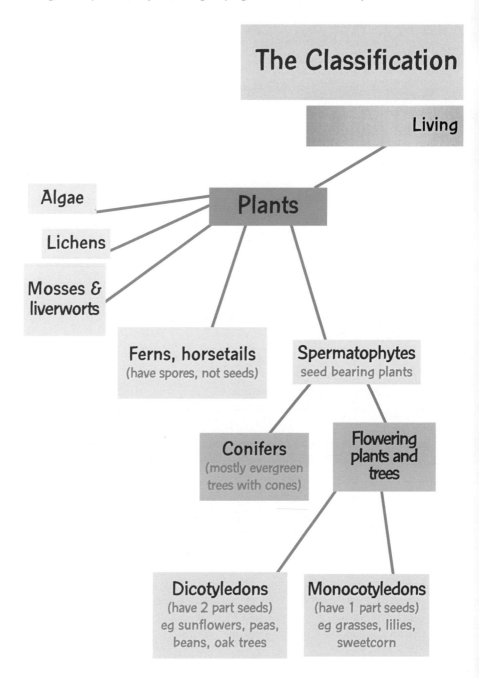

The Classification

Living

Plants

Algae

Lichens

Mosses & liverworts

Ferns, horsetails (have spores, not seeds)

Spermatophytes seed bearing plants

Conifers (mostly evergreen trees with cones)

Flowering plants and trees

Dicotyledons (have 2 part seeds) eg sunflowers, peas, beans, oak trees

Monocotyledons (have 1 part seeds) eg grasses, lilies, sweetcorn

# of Living Things

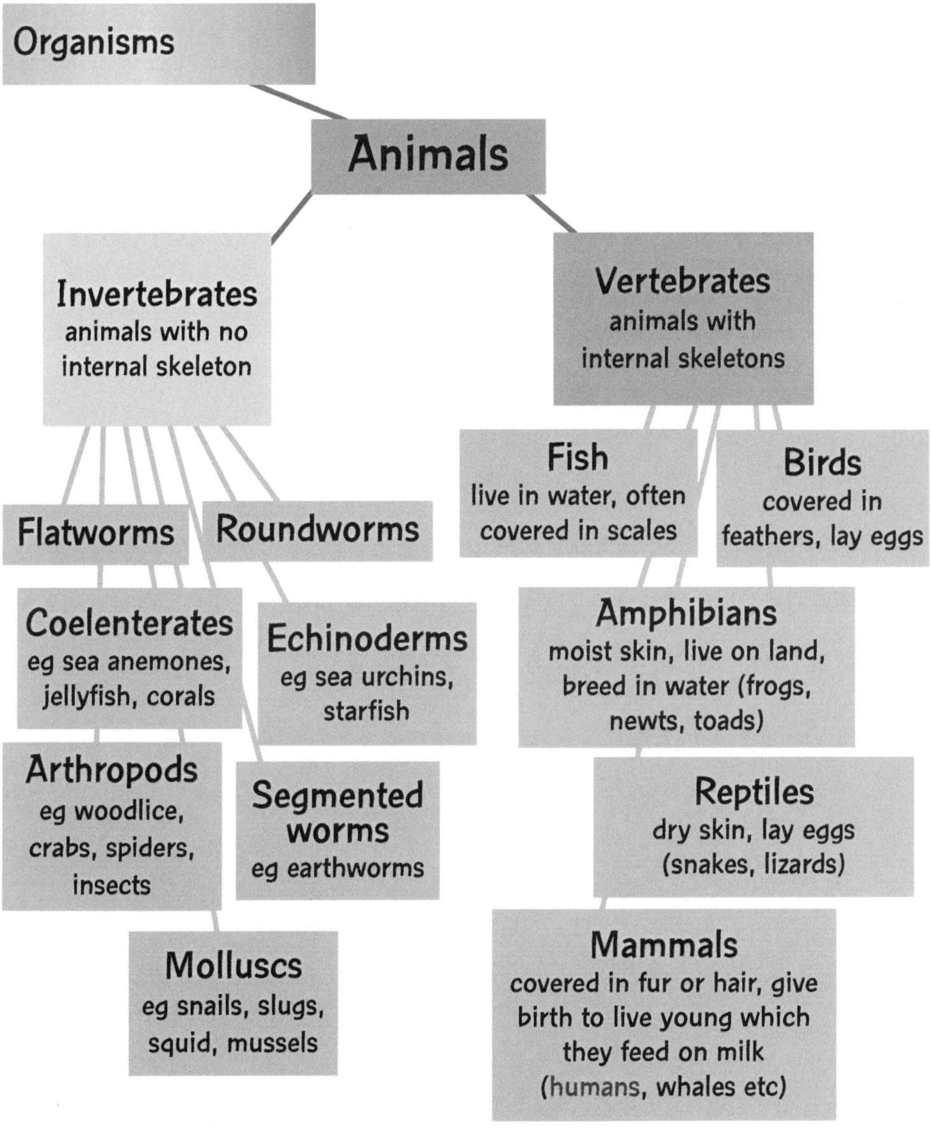

Organisms

Animals

Invertebrates
animals with no
internal skeleton

Vertebrates
animals with
internal skeletons

Flatworms

Roundworms

Fish
live in water, often
covered in scales

Birds
covered in
feathers, lay eggs

Coelenterates
eg sea anemones,
jellyfish, corals

Echinoderms
eg sea urchins,
starfish

Amphibians
moist skin, live on land,
breed in water (frogs,
newts, toads)

Arthropods
eg woodlice,
crabs, spiders,
insects

**Segmented
worms**
eg earthworms

Reptiles
dry skin, lay eggs
(snakes, lizards)

Molluscs
eg snails, slugs,
squid, mussels

Mammals
covered in fur or hair, give
birth to live young which
they feed on milk
(humans, whales etc)

Identifying animals

Invertebrates

Animals without an internal skeleton are called invertebrates. The most common invertebrates you will come across are:

Snails and slugs - **Molluscs**
Earthworms – **Segmented worms**
Woodlice – **Crustaceans**
Spiders – **Arthropods with 8 legs**
Beetles, bees, wasps and ladybirds – **Arthropods with 6 legs**
Centipedes and millipedes – **Arthropods with many legs**
Sea anemones – **Coelenterates**
Sea urchins and starfish – **Echinoderms**

Vertebrates

Animals with an internal skeleton are called vertebrates, or chordates. The characteristic features of the different vertebrate groups are:

Fish - have scaly skin, gills, live in water and are cold blooded.
Amphibians - have soft moist skin, lay eggs in water, and are cold blooded.
Reptiles - have dry scaly skin, lay eggs with leathery cases on land, and are cold blooded.
Birds - have feathers, lay eggs with hard shells and are warm blooded
Mammals - have hair, give birth to live young which they feed on milk, and are warm blooded.

Identifying trees

To help you identify trees, remember they can be divided into 2 main groups, broadleaves and conifers, based on the shape of their leaves:

Broadleaves - have flattened wide leaves. Most are deciduous and lose their leaves in the winter.
Conifers - have needle-like leaves and are usually evergreen and keep their leaves in winter.

Other features to look at when trying to identify trees are the shape and structure of the tree itself, the colour and texture of the bark, and any buds or flowers, fruit or seeds it may have.

The Little Book of Living Things

Broadleaves

Leaves are either simple or compound:

> Simple leaves consist of one leaf attached to the leaf stalk. These may be long and thin as in the willow, or roundish as in the beech.
> Compound leaves are made up of a number of leaflets or lobes.
> Palmate compound leaves have several leaflets arranged at the end of the leaf stalk as in the horsechestnut (palmate leaves are like a hand).
> Pinnate compound leaves have several leaflets growing out from the leaf stalk as in the ash.

Conifers

Different types of conifers can be identified from the shape, size and arrangement of their needles.

Supporting the Foundation Stage curriculum

'Learning for young children is a rewarding and enjoyable experience in which they explore, investigate, discover, create, practise, rehearse, repeat, revise and consolidate their developing knowledge, skills, understanding and attitudes. ' QCA.

What better way to stimulate children's interest than through learning about the natural environment and living things?
The activities in the Little Book of Living Things will help children to work towards the Early Learning Goals for:

Personal, Social and Emotional Development - dispositions and attitudes:
- be confident to try new activities, initiate ideas and speak in a familiar group;
- maintain attention, concentrate, and sit quietly when appropriate;
- continue to be interested, excited and motivated to learn.
  – self confidence & self-esteem:
- respond to significant experiences, showing a range of feelings when appropriate;
- have a developing awareness of their own needs, views and feelings and be sensitive to the needs, views and feelings of others.
  - making relationships:
- work as part of a group, taking turns and sharing fairly, understanding that there need to be agreed values and codes of behaviour for groups of people, including adults and children, to work together harmoniously.
  – behaviour and self-control:
- consider the consequences of their words and action for themselves & others.
  – self-care:
- select and use activities and resources independently.

Knowledge and Understanding of the World - exploration & investigation:
- investigate objects & materials by using all of their senses as appropriate;

- find out, & identify, some features of living things, objects, & events they observe;
- look closely at similarities, differences, patterns and change;
- ask questions about why things happen and how things work.
  - designing and making skills:
- build and construct with a wide range of objects, selecting appropriate resources and adapting their work where necessary.
  - ICT:
- find out and identify the uses of everyday technology and use information and communication technology to support their learning.
  - sense of time:
- differentiate between past and present;
- find out about the past and present events in their own lives, and in those of family members and other people they know.
  - sense of place:
- observe, find out and identify features in the place they live & the natural world;
- find out about their environment, and talk about those features they like & dislike.

Communication, Language and Literacy - language for communication:
- interact with others, negotiating plans & activities & taking turns in conversations;
- sustain active listening, responding to what they have heard by relevant comments, questions or actions;
- extend their vocabulary, exploring the meanings and sounds of new words.
  - language for thinking:
- use talk to organise, sequence and clarifying thinking, ideas, feelings & events.
  - reading:
- explore and experiment with sound, words and texts.
  - writing:
- attempt writing for different purposes, using features of different forms such as lists, stories and instructions.

Mathematical Development – numbers as labels and for counting:
- say and use number names in order in familiar contexts.
  - counting:
- use language such as 'more' or 'less' to compare two numbers.
  - shape, space and measures:
- use language such as 'greater', 'smaller', 'heavier' or 'lighter' to compare quantities;
- use everyday words to describe position;
- use developing mathematical ideas and methods to solve practical problems.

Physical Development - movement:
- move with confidence, imagination and safety;
- move with control and coordination.
  - health and bodily awareness:
- recognise the importance of keeping healthy & those things which contribute to this;
- recognise the changes that happen to bodies when they are active.
  - using equipment, tools and materials:
- use a range of small and large equipment;
- handle tools, objects, construction & malleable materials safely & with control.

Creative Development – imagination:
- use imagination in art & design, music, dance, imaginative role play & stories.
  - responding to experiences, expressing & communicating ideas:
- respond in a variety of ways to what they see, hear, smell, touch and feel.

The Little Book of Living Things

Life Processes

This section of the Little Book of Living Things focuses on the seven life processes which are common to all living things, both plants and animals. The following background information is a reminder of what these life processes are:

Nutrition   Animals eat plants or other animals.
            Plants are able to make their own food by using energy from sunlight to convert carbon dioxide and water into carbohydrates. This process is called photosynthesis and occurs in the leaves and green parts of the plant.

Movement   All animals move, in different ways depending on the structure of their bodies.
            Plants are anchored in the soil by their roots and so are unable to move from place to place. Instead, their leaves and flowers move in response to external stimuli such as light.

Growth   Most animals grow until they reach their optimum size at maturity. Growth then becomes confined to repairing damaged tissue.
            Plants generally carry on getting bigger all their lives.

Respiration Respiration in animals is the process whereby the energy stored in food is released to support all the other life processes. Respiration involves breathing in oxygen from the air and, transporting this oxygen around the body in the blood stream. A chemical reaction in the cells of the body releases the energy.
            During respiration in plants, food molecules stored in the cells of the plant are broken down and energy is released.

Reproduction All living things die eventually, but are able to produce offspring to ensure that they survive as a species. Mammals, including humans, usually have small numbers of young and invest a great deal of effort in rearing them to maturity. Other animals such as fish and frogs, and most plants produce very large numbers of young which then 'fend for themselves'.

Senses   Animals use their senses to find food and avoid danger.
            Different senses are important to different animals – as humans we rely very much on our sense of sight.
            All plants respond to the stimuli of light and gravity while some, such as the venus fly trap and mimosa are adapted to respond to touch.

Excretion   All living things produce waste which they have to get rid of. In animals this includes urine and faeces and carbon dioxide, a waste product of respiration which is removed when they breathe out.
            Plants excrete waste gases during the process of respiration and deciduous plants lose waste material annually when their leaves fall.

Living every day

Focus: Life processes

This activity provides a natural way in to talking about life processes with young children. It builds on their knowledge of daily routines and can be used as a starting point for thinking about life processes which are common to all living things. Having built up a picture of what we do every day you can then go on to use the activities in the rest of this section of the book to investigate different life processes in more detail.

Talk with the children about the different things they do every day. Help them to remember things they do before they arrive at the setting as well as thing they do when they leave at the end of the day. You may want to use pictures and drawings to illustrate the different activities taking place during the day.

Look out for:

* Be aware of the age and stage of development of the children. Don't let it get too complicated!
* Children come from families with varied structures and organisation. Don't exclude anyone.

Key words

* day
* night
* wash
* break-
  fast
* lunch
* tea
* supper
* out
* home
* shops
* clean
* drink
* feel
* smell
* eat
* move
* toilet

The Little Book of Living Things

What you need

* photos of children involved in activities throughout the day
* pictures of places, rooms etc
* clock
* time line (a washing line and pegs would be helpful)

Things to do

* Pegging pictures, drawings or photos on a washing line helps children with order, and enables you to rearrange the items for different children, or to add new items as children remember them!
* At the end of the discussion you will come up with a pattern of the day (or for younger children, a part of the day) which looks something like this:

waking up	(movement,	senses)
getting up	(movement,	senses)
going to the toilet	(excretion,	senses)
having breakfast	(nutrition,	senses)
coming to nursery	(movement,	senses)
playing with friends	(movement,	senses)
eating a snack	(nutrition,	senses)
going to the toilet	(excretion,	senses)
washing my hands	(movement,	senses)
having lunch	(nutrition,	senses)
going to the toilet	(excretion,	senses)
going home	(movement,	senses)
going to the shops	(movement,	senses)
playing outside	(movement,	senses)
watching TV	(senses)	
having tea/dinner	(nutrition,	senses)
having a bath	(movement,	senses)
having a story	(senses)	
going to bed	(movement)	

From this list you can begin to see all the opportunities for talking about different life processes and developing children's awareness of them.
The areas which may not come up immediately are:

Respiration – breathing is something we do automatically and may not be mentioned during the discussion.

Growth – setting up activities which children can re-visit regularly over an extended time period helps with a sense of growth and time passing.

Reproduction – Spring and early Summer are good times to focus children's attention on the birth of new babies in the animal kingdom.

The activities included in the remainder of this section of the book focus on each of the life processes in turn.

What Shall we Eat Today?

Focus: Nutrition

Context: All animals, including humans, need to eat to stay alive. Helping children to experience different types of food will start to build an awareness of the importance of eating a healthy balanced diet. It also provides an opportunity to understand that we all enjoy different types of food depending on where we live, what our family eats, or what our religious or cultural beliefs are.

Just a reminder:

We eat regularly to give us the energy we need to grow, move and stay warm. To stay healthy we need to eat the right balance of protein, carbohydrate and fat, and to drink sufficient water every day.

Some animals, such as cats and lions eat only meat and are called carnivores.

Others such as cows, sheep and elephants eat only plants and are called herbivores.

Animals which eat meat and plants are called omnivores. Humans are omnivores but some people are vegetarians and don't eat meat. Most birds are omnivores, eating meat and plants.

Look out for:

* Some children may be allergic to some types of food - eg nuts or dairy products.
* Use cooking or food preparation activities to teach children how to behave safely when handling hot objects or sharp knives.
* Teach children basic food hygiene rules including the importance of washing their hands properly.

Key words

* food
* fruit
* veget-ables
* break-fast
* lunch
* tea
* supper
* dinner
* snack
* drink
* water
* peel
* cut
* chop
* slice

What you need

* recipe books
* magazines with pictures of food
* magnifiers
* a basket of fruit and vegetables – including some unusual ones

Things to do

* Talk with the children about the different meals they have during the day. Use this opportunity to emphasise the importance of eating breakfast every morning.
* Using picture books, illustrated recipe books and pictures from magazines, talk about the different types of food we eat.
* Encourage the children to talk about the foods they like to eat. Help them to find pictures of their favourite foods.
* Provide a basket containing lots of different fruit and vegetables.
* Encourage the children to explore the contents of the basket and observe closely using all their senses
* Talk with the children about how different fruit and vegetables feel, smell and look. Some may even make interesting sounds if you tap or shake them.
* See how many different ways the children can think of to sort the contents of the basket.
* Discuss which ingredients would be good to mix together in a salad – a fruit salad, vegetable salad, or a mixture.
* Help the children to peel, cut and slice the ingredients to make the salads they have described.
* Enjoy eating the final product.

You could also try....

‣ providing the ingredients for children to make their own sandwiches for an indoor or outdoor picnic.
‣ asking parents from different ethnic backgrounds to talk about the types of food they eat and how they are prepared.
‣ preparing and cooking the vegetables you have grown in your outdoor area.
‣ arranging a visit to a local market, supermarket or café.

Songs, rhymes, stories

‣ Pat a Cake, Pat a Cake
‣ I'm a Little Teapot
‣ Polly Put the Kettle on
‣ Jelly on the Plate
‣ Five Currant Buns
‣ Jack Sprat Could eat no Fat
‣ Handa's Surprise
‣ Oliver's Fruit Salad

Feed the Birds

Focus: Nutrition

Context: Attracting birds into the garden area around your setting will provide lots of interest for children all through the year. Children will have the opportunity to see and recognise different species and become aware of the different types of food they eat. Remember to put out different sorts of food and to cater for birds that feed in different ways and at different heights.

Just a reminder:

Different bird species will be attracted by different types of food.

Provide the birds with a supply of fresh water (to drink and bathe in) as well as food.

Once you start to feed the birds they will rely on you! Think about how you will cover weekends and holidays.

Don't over-fill bird feeding places, specially the ones near the ground. Left over food may attract predators or vermin.

Look out for:

* Make sure children understand that bird food is for the birds to eat, not them.
* Be aware of any children who have peanut allergies.
* Remind children to wash their hands after handling animal food of any sort.

Key words

* bird	* breast	* hang
* beak	* feather	* table
* wing	* seed	* hook
* head	* nut	* window
* feet	* peanut	* peck
* food	* water	

The Little Book of Living Things

What you need

* bird food – seeds, nuts, breadcrumbs
* bird feeders – made or bought
* binoculars
* illustrated books about birds
* clip and white boards

Things to do

* Talk with the children about what they already know about birds.
* Look at pictures of common garden birds and help the children to notice how they differ from one another. Talk about colour, size, shape; shape or colour of their beaks, legs, feathers etc.
* Discuss what birds like to eat, and where they might find their food.
* Look at the different types of bird food you have available – talk about the size, shape, colour and texture of the nuts and seeds. (If you are brave you could include mealworms - a particular favourite of robins).
* Go out into the garden area and decide with the children where you might put your bird feeders. You will want to be able to see the feeders easily from indoors, but they need to be high enough up to be safe from cats.
* To make the bird spotting more exciting you could create an indoor bird hide by covering one of the windows at child height with black paper and then cutting peep holes in for the children to peer out from.
* Remind the children to check regularly to see which birds come to their bird feeders to feed.
* Help them to use the binoculars to observe the birds more closely and provide pictures and reference books so they can identify the birds they see.
* When you are refilling the bird feeders talk about the different birds the children have seen and which food they like to eat.

You could also try....

▸ helping the children to record the times of day when the birds come to the feeder.
▸ keeping a tally of the different bird species that visit the outdoor area.
▸ setting up the role play area as a bird hide.
▸ visiting a local park to feed the ducks.
▸ looking at pictures of birds from different habitats – seabirds, birds of prey, flightless birds.

Songs, rhymes, stories

▸ Two Little Dickie Birds
▸ Five Little Ducks
▸ The North Wind Doth Blow, and we shall have snow
▸ The Wise Old Owl Sat in an Oak
▸ The Owl Who Was Afraid of the Dark

The Little Book of Living Things

How Do Animals Move?

Focus: Movement

Context: All animals move, but in different ways. How an animal moves depends on its body structure, where it lives and how it has adapted to the environment it inhabits. Animals move to find food, water and shelter and to escape from danger.

Just a reminder:

Vertebrates such as humans have an internal skeleton made up of bones.
Where the bones meet there are joints which enable parts of the body such as arms and legs to bend as we move.
Pairs of muscles attached to the bones contract and relax as we move.
The energy to make muscles comes from the food we eat.
Invertebrates don't have an internal skeleton and move in different ways depending on the structure of their body.

Look out for:

* Make sure there is enough open space for children to move around freely without bumping into things or each other.
* This is a good activity for out of doors.

Key words

* arm
* leg
* hand
* finger
* elbow
* knee
* head
* shoulder
* foot
* toe
* walk
* run
* crawl
* fly
* swim
* hop
* climb
* skip
* joint
* bend

What you need

* photos of people showing arms, legs etc.
* drawings of a human skeleton
* space for a group to move around
* books and pictures showing animals moving in different ways – walking, running, crawling, hopping, flying, swimming etc.

Things to do

* Use the photographs and pictures as a starting point for a discussion about parts of the body.
* Play a game of 'Heads, Shoulders, Knees and Toes' or 'Simon Says'.
* Help the children to think about all the different ways in which they could move from one place to another. Try these out, individually or as part of a 'Follow the Leader' game.
* Talk about the different parts of the body that they are using when moving in different ways.
* Using books, pictures and photographs, help the children to put together a collection of pictures of animals moving in different ways. For example:

  birds – flying, walking, swimming
  worms – wriggling and crawling
  fish – swimming
  frogs – hopping
  monkeys – climbing and swinging
  horses - galloping and jumping

* Play a game of 'Guess what I am?' A child thinks of an animal and imitates how it moves. All the other children have to try and guess which animal it is.
* If you are looking after any minibeasts in your setting – worms, snails, stick insects or spiders – use this as an opportunity to look closely at how they move.

You could also try....

‣ making up a dance with the children to mimic the way different animals move.
‣ comparing the movement of fingers and toes by playing a game which involves children trying to pick small objects up with their toes.
‣ setting up the role play corner as a veterinary surgery.
‣ offer animal masks or puppets to help children feel animal movements; or make a role play jungle, zoo or farm.

Songs, rhymes, stories

‣ There's a Worm at the Bottom of the Garden
‣ Row Row Row the Boat
‣ One Finger, One Thumb
‣ Okey Cokey
‣ The Hare and the Tortoise
‣ Funny Bones ; J & A Ahlberg
‣ Duck's Ditty ; Walter de la Mare

Can a Plant Move?

Focus: Movement

Context: Plants move, although in a less obvious way from animals because they have their roots anchored in the soil. Movement in plants happens relatively slowly, providing a good opportunity to draw children's attention to small changes occurring over a longer period of time.

Just a reminder:

Because they are dependant on light as a source of energy, plants respond to light by turning towards it. Roots grow downwards and shoots grow upwards because of the way different parts of a plant respond to the influence of gravity.

Climbing plants often provide good examples of movement as their tendrils curl around supports and help the plant to reach upwards towards the light.

Look out for:

* Only grow plants and seeds you know are safe to handle.
* Make sure children wash their hands after handling plants or seeds or being involved in any gardening activity.
* Provide suitable sized gardening tools for children to use.
* Remind them not to eat the seeds.

Key words

* seed
* plant
* cress
* water
* compost
* pot
* light
* sweet pea
* sunflower
* turn
* tendril
* climb

cress

What you need

* cress seeds
* cotton wool, pieces of old towel or blotting paper
* small plastic containers
* sweet pea and sunflower seeds
* plastic pots
* seed compost
* magnifying glasses

Things to do

Growing cress indoors

* Look carefully at the cress and other seeds you have ready to plant.
* Talk with the children about how the seeds differ from one another - size, shape, colour, texture.
* Using the cress seeds, work with the children to put a layer of towel, cotton wool or blotting paper in the bottom of the plastic containers.
* Pour on enough water to make the layer damp, and sprinkle a good covering of cress seeds over the surface.
* Put the containers on a window sill and keep them damp.
* Remind the children to check their seeds every day to keep them damp and then see what happens.
* Talk about the changes which happen as the cress seeds start to grow.
* Help the children to take photographs and make drawings of the plants.
* When the cress is 2-3 cm high it will be possible to see the plants turning towards the light.
* Encourage the children to look closely and see how the stems bend over so the leaves are exposed to the daylight coming in through the window.
* Turn the containers round, leave the plants for a few hours and then look again to see which way they have turned.

You could also try growing sunflowers and sweet peas outdoors

▸ Help the children to plant some sweet pea and sunflower seeds in individual small pots.
▸ Keep the compost damp and watch out for signs of the young plants beginning to grow.
▸ Go outside with the children to choose suitable places for the plants to be transplanted - both sweet peas and sunflowers need a sunny spot.
▸ Transplant the sweet peas to a sunny area where they can climb upwards – fix some netting to a wall or fence to support them.
▸ Help the children to find the tendrils on the pea plant and see how they curl round the supports to help the plant move upwards.
▸ When the sunflowers are in bloom help the children to notice how the flower heads turn during the day to track the course of the sun.

Look What I can do Now

Focus: Growth

Context: Looking at how humans grow and change as they get older is an ideal way to support and practice children's developing skills and competencies. It helps children to appreciate change over time and may create opportunities to talk sensitively about birth and death.

Just a reminder:

Animals grow in size until they reach maturity - in humans this is usually around 18 years of age.

Once animals have reached their optimum size their growth is confined to the repair of damaged tissue for instance when we cut ourselves, or break a bone.

Plants keep on growing till they die, although some grow very slowly.

Look out for:

* When discussing families be sensitive to the many different family groupings which exist.
* Remember not to give the message that 'bigger is better'.

Key words

* baby
* toddler
* child
* teenager
* adult
* young
* old
* small
* big
* bigger
* mother
* father
* clothes
* shoes
* tall
* grow

The Little Book of Living Things

What you need

* photos of the children in your setting as babies, and of their parents, brothers and sisters and other family members
* some baby clothes, shoes and toys
* a height chart or measuring stick
* a digital camera

Things to do

* Ask the children's parents to provide some pictures of the children as babies, and as toddlers. You could add some of your own!
* Take some individual photographs of the children in your setting – if you have a digital camera you could let the children take these pictures themselves.
* Look at the pictures with the children, helping them to notice similarities and differences.
* Help them to sequence the photographs and discuss the people they see – what clothes they are wearing, what they are doing - lying down, sitting up or moving around. This is an opportunity to use the language of extended time – weeks, months and years.
* Discuss how height changes as they have grown older. Look at the sizes of hands and feet. Talk about 'growing out' of clothes and shoes and illustrate this with examples of baby clothes.
* Set up a measuring chart in one area of your setting. Organise height measuring sessions at regular intervals during the year so children can see how much they have grown.
* Talk about what babies, children and adults are able to do. Can children remember what they could do at different ages?
* Emphasise what they can already do, what they are almost able to do and what they will be able to do when they are older. This is a good opportunity to build up a Can Do chart for each child emphasising their competencies.

You could also try....

▶ inviting a parent with a new born baby to come in and talk to the children.
▶ organising a visit from your local health visitor.
▶ helping the children to create their own personal book containing their pictures and Can Do chart.
▶ recreating the health visitor's clinic in the role play area.

Songs, rhymes, stories

▶ Avocado Baby; John Burningham
▶ The Baby Catalogue; Janet and Alan Ahlberg
▶ Titch; Pat Hutchins
▶ Alfie's Clothes; Shirley Hughes
▶ Alfie's Feet; Shirley Hughes

The Little Book of Living Things

How Big are the Beans Now?

Focus: Growth

Context: Watching seeds germinate and start to grow is an exciting investigation which helps children to see the early stages of a plant life cycle. Once the beans have sprouted they grow and change rapidly so there is something new to see every day, encouraging children to look closely and to revisit an activity regularly.

Just a reminder:

Plants such as broad beans produce seeds which will grow into new plants the following season. Inside the tough outer coating of the seed are the two halves of the bean which act as a food store for the embryo bean plant. You can just see this between the two halves of the seed - a tiny root and two tiny leaves. When the bean is soaked, it begins to swell, the germination process starts and the tiny plant begins to grow. When planted in the earth the seed acts as a food store until the plant has grown into daylight; the leaves turn green and use energy from the sun to turn carbon dioxide in the air into food through the process called photosynthesis.

Look out for:

* Soak the broad beans first to make them easier to handle, and to speed germination.
* Make sure children understand that the seeds are not for eating.
* Always wash your hands after handling plants and seeds.
* **Never** use red kidney beans   they are poisonous until fully cooked.

Key words

* beans
* peas
* seeds
* plant
* leaf
* root
* food
* shoot
* grow
* water
* damp
* soil

What you need

* clear plastic picnic tumblers
* blotting paper cut to the right size to fit around the inside of the tumblers
* broad bean seeds, soaked overnight
* stand magnifier

Things to do

* Look at the soaked broad bean seeds with the children and compare them with seeds which haven't been soaked. Talk with them about the differences they notice - in size, shape, colour, texture and smell.
* Help the children to peel off the outer coating from one or two of the seeds and gently prise the two halves of the seed apart. Encourage them to look carefully at the tiny plant inside the seed – use a stand magnifier if you have one.
* Using the remaining soaked broad beans, show the children how to line the inside of the tumbler with a piece of blotting paper. Gently push the seed down so it is trapped between the paper and the side of the tumbler.
* Encourage the children to set up their own bean jars and to pour a small amount of water into the bottom of the tumbler to keep the bean moist.
* Discuss where to put the beans so they can be kept damp and so you can look at them at every day. Agree a regular routine for examining the beans daily to see how they have changed.
* Look together carefully at the changes as the beans start to grow. What does the root do? What happens to the leaves?
* Help the children to make a visual record of the growth of the beans through drawings and photographs. Record their comments.
* Plant the bean plants in the garden and watch for more beans to grow.

You could also try....

▸ making a display of the children's drawings, photographs and comments about the growing beans.
▸ providing the resources to change the role play area into a garden centre.
▸ planting pumpkin seeds to produce fruit which can be harvested in the autumn.

Songs, rhymes, stories

▸ Jack and the Beanstalk
▸ The Enormous Turnip
▸ Oats and Beans and Barley Grow
▸ Mary, Mary Quite Contrary

What happens when I run?

Focus: **Respiration**

Context: Breathing is something which we are not usually aware of until we stop and think about it. Running around, or jumping up and down on the spot, and then stopping to listen to our breathing is a good way of drawing children's attention to this essential part of staying alive. This is also a good opportunity to reinforce the importance of regular exercise for health and well being.

Just a reminder:

Breathing is only one part of the whole process known as respiration, but it is the one which young children will be able to recognise most readily. Your lungs are situated in an airtight sac inside your rib cage. When you breathe in, the muscles attached to your ribs contract and lift your rib cage up as your diaphragm flattens. This causes your lungs to expand with air flowing in to them through your nose and mouth. When the muscles relax your rib cage falls, the chest cavity gets smaller and air is squeezed out of your lungs as you breathe out. When you exercise, your muscles need extra energy quickly, so your heart beats faster and you breathe rapidly.

Look out for:

* Be sensitive to those children who cannot move around easily - find alternative ways to help them to exercise.
* Be careful the children don't hyperventilate (breathe in and out very quickly) as this will make them feel dizzy. This can easily be relieved by sitting quietly for a while.

Key words

* breathe	* walk
* in	* run
* out	* chest
* fast	* lungs
* slow	* ribs
* jump	* heart

What you need

* books with simple pictures of the inside of the human body, showing the position of the lungs and the heart
* stethoscope if you have one - the ones in children's doctors' kits work surprisingly well
* mirrors

Things to do

* Use the pictures in books to discuss with the children the different parts of the body and what they are called.
* Ask them to sit as still as possible and feel whether there is any part of their body which is still moving. Show them how to put their hands on their chests so they can feel their rib cage moving up and down.
* Explain how to exaggerate this process by taking a big deep breath in, holding it, and then breathing out again.
* Now jump up and down on the spot for one minute, or run around fast outside, and then stop and stand still. What do they notice?
* Talk about how fast they are breathing – the origin of the expression being 'out of breath'.
* Do they notice how fast their heart is beating? Can they feel their heart beating in their chest? Try using a stethoscope to listen to each other's breathing and heartbeat.
* Repeat the exercise a few times. What other side effects of exercise do children notice? (hot, red, sweating, tired)
* Make this pause a regular feature of outdoor play sessions.
* Watch what happens when they are out of breath on a cold day. This is a really good time to observe themselves breathing at rest and after exertion.

You could also try....

▸ organising a visit from a paramedic
▸ starting a fitness campaign in your setting – this could include: *encouraging children and adults to walk to the setting; playing outside whatever the weather; being active in some way every day.*
▸ setting up the role play area as a doctor's surgery or ambulance station.
▸ organising a summer mini Olympics, with events suitable for all ages and abilities.

Songs, rhymes, stories

Try playing these games:
▸ Cat and Mouse
▸ Stick in the Mud
▸ Hide and Seek
▸ Tails
▸ Statues

The Gingerbread Man
Song 'Healthy Heart' from Taking Care of Myself

The Little Book of Living Things

What Will This Seed Grow into?

Focus: Growth

Context: Growing plants from seeds helps children to experience and begin to understand the life cycle of flowering plants. It gives an opportunity to follow change over time and encourages children to be aware of the importance of looking after plants on a daily basis. There is the added bonus of growing something you can eat, prompting further investigation of where different types of food come from.

Just a reminder:

Plants grow and increase in size throughout their lifetime. At certain stages, depending on the type of plant, they produce specialised structures called flowers which contain their reproductive organs. Inside the flower are the male and female parts. The male parts are called stamens and produce pollen and the female parts are called the carpel and include the ovary and the ovules. During fertilisation pollen is transferred from the stamen to the carpel either by the wind or by insects. The fertilised ovules then grow into seeds to produce the next generation of plants.

Look out for:

* This is a long term project which needs to be managed carefully to see it through to completion. Pumpkins are unlikely to be fully mature until the Autumn, and will need watering right through the summer.

Key words

* seed
* plant
* compost
* pot
* grow
* water
* leaf
* flower
* fruit
* vegetable
* insect
* petal

What you need

* a selection of seeds for planting – melons, pumpkins, tomatoes
* plant pots, seed compost, labels
* grow bags
* notebook and camera to record plant growth and development
* seed catalogues and gardening magazines

Things to do

* Talk with the children about all the different types of flowers and vegetables they know of.
* Use seed catalogues and gardening magazines to prompt ideas and discussion.
* Plant a range of different seeds in trays or pots in the setting. Try marrows, pumpkins or tomatoes.
* When the seedlings have started to grow well transfer them to a prepared garden plot, grow bag or large container. Help the children to look after the plants carefully, ensuring they are watered regularly, have sufficient light to help them grow well and are not eaten by slugs, snails or greenfly.
* Record the development of the plants through pictures and photographs. Encourage the children to keep a simple record of when the seeds germinate, how quickly they grow and when the first flowers appear.
* Talk about the colour and scent of the flowers and encourage the children to observe the plants regularly to spot any insects visiting the flowers.
* Check regularly to see what happens after the flowers have been pollinated. Look out for the petals dropping off and the ovule swelling up and forming a fruiting body – a baby marrow, pumpkin or tomato.
* Keep the plants well watered and support their vigorous growth with regular doses of liquid fertiliser. Harvest the vegetables when fully formed.
* Cut the vegetables open and help the children to examine them carefully, using a hand magnifier so you can identify the seeds inside.

You could also try....

▸ using the marrows, tomatoes or pumpkins in different recipes – cheese and tomato sandwiches, chutney, stuffed marrow, pumpkin soup or pumpkin pie.
▸ linking to Autumn activities on the theme of the seasons and harvest.
▸ turning the role play area into a market stall to sell the produce you have grown.

Songs, rhymes, stories

▸ Peter, Peter Pumpkin Eater.
▸ One Man Went to Mow
▸ Oliver's Vegetables; by Vivian French
▸ Tilda's Seeds; by Melanie Eclare

Whose Baby am I?

Focus: Nutrition

Context: This activity focuses on the animal kingdom and the many different opportunities which you can use to draw children's attention to the need for two parents, one male and one female in order for babies to be created. Use the information in this book to develop your setting as a breeding ground for as wide a range of minibeasts, amphibians and birds as possible.

Just a reminder:

Mammals give birth to babies which are miniature versions of themselves. All other vertebrates - birds, fish, amphibians and reptiles - hatch from eggs and resemble their parents.
Some invertebrates, such as worms and spiders hatch from eggs looking like their parents, but several - butterflies and moths for example - go through a complex life cycle known as metamorphosis. This involves a complete change in their body structure as they develop from egg to caterpillar to chrysalis to adult.

Look out for:

* Be careful not to disturb animals during the breeding season
* Ensure children wash their hands after handling or touching animals.

Key words

* baby   * hatch
* egg   * birth
* grow   * small
* adult   * bigger
* mother   * change
* father   * grow

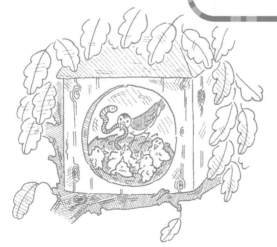

What you need

* pictures and photographs of baby animals and their parents – include mammals, birds, fish, reptiles, amphibians and a range of invertebrates; information books
* areas around your setting where you have provided conditions for different animals to breed

Things to do

Comparing babies and adults

* With the children look at a selection of pictures of baby animals. Include as wide a variety as possible – pets, native wild animals, birds, fish, reptiles, invertebrates.
* Encourage the children to look closely and describe what they see.
* Ask them what they think the babies are doing, how they eat, how they move around, and how they keep safe. This helps to extend children's vocabulary as well as reinforcing their understanding of the basic life processes common to all living things.
* Compare the baby animals with their parents, and talk about all the different ways in which the babies will change as they grow into adults.

Finding examples of animal babies

* In the spring and early summer go on a hunt for small creatures in your outdoor area. Look out for examples of baby worms, woodlice, snails, spiders and beetles. You could bring these in to the setting for a short period of time to enable the children to observe them more closely.
* Set up bird boxes around the grounds to encourage different species to breed. Encourage the children to watch these carefully to detect any evidence of newly hatched baby birds.
* A small pond area may attract frogs and toads to breed.
* Plant a butterfly garden with attractive plants and flowers.

You could also try....

▸ turning the role play area into a zoological park or a farm.
▸ visiting a local zoo or farm at the time when new babies are being born.
▸ inviting someone who breeds birds or small animals to visit your setting and talk to the children.
▸ visiting a local park in the Spring to see ducklings with their parents.

Songs, rhymes, stories

▸ The Elephants went in Two by Two
▸ The Berenstein Bears' New Baby
▸ The Ugly Duckling

What Can You See?

Context: Sight is the most dominant of the five senses, and the one we rely on most.
This activity provides lots of opportunities for children to look closely, spending time observing
and noticing things in the world around them. It also develops their manipulative skills through
the use of magnifiers and binoculars, and by using fine felt pens and pencils for drawing.

Just a reminder:

We see things around us when light bounces off the surface of the object and enters our eyes.
The light passes through the pupil - the black circle in the centre of our eye. It is focused by the
lens onto the retina on the back surface of the eyeball. The nerves in the retina are stimulated by
the light and send messages along the optic nerve to a specialised area of the brain.
The brain then decodes these messages and tells us what it is we are seeing.

Look out for:

* Be sensitive to children who have
  impaired vision.
* When outdoors, warn children never to
  look directly at the sun, particularly when
  using binoculars or a telescope.

Key words

* see
* look
* eye
* notice
* inside
* outside
* bigger
* smaller
* glasses
* magni-
  fier
* light
* binoc-
  ulars

The Little Book of Living Things

What you need

* hand magnifiers
* stand/table top magnifier if possible
* child sized binoculars
* a selection of fruit and vegetables
  - try to include some unusual ones
  - a kiwi fruit, sprout, apple, star
  fruit, broccoli, tomato
* seeds and seed heads– soaked peas or beans, clematis seeds, dandelions, teasels
* drawing paper, fine felt pens and coloured pencils

Things to do

* Examine the fruit and vegetables together, encouraging the children to look closely and describe all the different features they can see. Discuss what the children think each fruit or vegetable might look like inside – make a note of their ideas and comments.
* Cut open the fruits and vegetables and help the children to look closely at the inside. If they need it, demonstrate how to use a hand or table magnifier to help them to see more clearly.
* A table top or stand magnifier will make it easier for the children to see the magnified images more clearly.
* Encourage the children to draw what they can see using the magnifiers – using fine tipped pens and coloured pencils. Display these alongside the words the children used to describe the things they were looking at.
* Repeat the activity using the seed and seed head collection.
* Now encourage the children to use hand magnifiers around the setting to look closely at plants and minibeasts, indoors and out.
* Help the children to use a pair of binoculars, demonstrating how to use the focus wheel and how to adjust the distance apart of the eye pieces. Encourage them to become proficient in using binoculars by setting up bird feeders around your setting (see page 14/15).

You could also try....

▸ setting up the role play area as an opticians.
▸ playing a game involving finding a route round the setting blindfolded, following instructions given by the other children.
▸ investigating light, dark and shadow – see 'The Little Book of Light & Shadow'.
▸ looking at pictures of animals that live in the dark, or live underground – moles, rabbits, worms etc.

Songs, rhymes, stories

▸ I See the Moon
▸ Peepo
▸ Where's Spot?

I Like That Smell

Focus: Senses

Context: Our sense of smell is often less developed than our sense of sight. Other animals rely very heavily on their sense of smell to find food and sense danger.
Smells can be very evocative and cause us to instantly remember special events, places, people and occasions.

Just a reminder:

Smells are formed by tiny particles or molecules floating in the air. When we smell things these molecules dissolve in the damp lining of mucus inside our nose and activate the smell receptors. These receptors then send messages along the nerves to the brain.
Our sense of smell is very closely related to our sense of taste   when we have a cold or a blocked nose we cannot taste things easily. The smell of food cooking can trigger salivation (mouth watering) in anticipation of eating something good.

Look out for:

* Some children may strongly dislike certain smells. Remember children with a blocked nose won't find this activity easy.
* Be aware that certain children may be allergic to pollen or react badly to certain flower scents. Remind children not to eat any of the foods they are investigating by smell.

Key words

* smell
* nose
* sniff
* scent
* food
* strong
* flower
* perfume
* cooking
* like
* dislike
* leaf

What you need

* a selection of strong scents which children will recognise (perfume, disinfectant, fruit squash, tomato ketchup, shampoo, onion etc
* small film canisters or similar opaque containers
* cotton wool

Things to do

* Talk with the children about their favourite smells. Encourage them to think about different smells they are aware of in the environment around them at home and in your setting.
* Make up different words to describe some of these smells and scents.
* Fill some of the containers with strongly perfumed or smelly liquids or objects. Cover the substance with cotton wool to encourage use of the sense of smell. Play a guessing game where children have to recognise an object just by its smell – start with fairly easy examples such as banana, lemon, onion, chocolate.
* Move on to more subtle examples such as different flowers, herbs or spices; or household perfumes, guessing which room they come from.
* Collect some other smelly things to try - perfumed candles, pot pourri, strongly scented flowers (such as carnations, hyacinths, lilac), air fresheners, empty perfume bottles. (Check for allergies among the group).
* Go on a 'smell safari' around your setting, in the park, down the street. Stop and breathe in to see what you can smell - take-away, fish and chips, tarmac, leaves, diesel, tyres, petrol, helping the children to focus on the smells which predominate in different areas, indoors and outdoors.
* Always use snack time and cooking as an opportunity to explore smells of fruit, cooking ingredients, toast, baking etc.

You could also try....

‣ making two matching pots of each smell for a matching game.
‣ growing herbs and other perfumed plants in your garden.
‣ providing opportunities for them to try and guess what is for lunch from the smell coming from the kitchen.
‣ providing opportunities for children to experiment with making their own perfumes – rose petal perfume for example.

Songs, rhymes, stories

‣ Five Currant Buns in a Baker's Shop
‣ Hot Cross Buns
‣ Lavender's Blue, Dilly Dilly
‣ Pat-a-cake, Pat-a-cake

Who Made That Noise?

Focus: Senses

Context: Sounds are all around us, inside and outside but we don't always hear them unless we concentrate. Helping children to 'tune in' to the world around them encourages their auditory perception, a vital skill to support their ongoing learning.

Just a reminder:

We hear things when sound vibrations travelling through the air reach our ears. The sound vibrations move down the ear canal until they reach the eardrum and cause it to vibrate too. The three small bones of the inner ear magnify these vibrations and pass them on to the fluid inside the cochlea. Small nerve endings inside the cochlea are then stimulated and send messages to the brain.

Look out for:

* Some children in your setting may have impaired hearing, either permanent or temporary.
* Many children, specially boys, suffer bouts of temporary hearing loss during the winter. If you suspect this, contact your manager or the child's parents.

Key words

* ear
* listen
* sound
* noise
* talk
* sing
* music
* record
* loud
* soft
* low
* high

What you need

* an opportunity for a group of children to be somewhere quiet in your setting (indoors or out) – where they can concentrate on listening
* a tape recorder
* magazines and catalogues to cut pictures from
* a selection of musical instruments – home made and commercial

Things to do

* Encourage the children to sit quietly indoors, close their eyes and listen carefully to the different sounds they can hear.
* Talk about these sounds and help them to identify them. Make up descriptive words to describe the sounds that they can hear.
* Talk about the sounds they like and the sounds they dislike; loud and soft noises, sudden and continuous ones.
* Repeat this activity in the outside area or garden of your setting. Are there some sounds you only hear indoors, and some you only hear outdoors?
* Which sounds are made by living things, and which are made by things which are not alive?
* Now show the children how to use a tape recorder to record different sounds around the setting.
* Help the children to make a sound effects tape – you could include:

children playing	an adult telling a story
a telephone ringing	a door bell
a TV or radio	a refrigerator humming
water running down a pipe	rain drumming on a roof
a car or lorry driving by	a toilet flushing
birds singing	a wind chime

* Use magazines and catalogues to look for pictures to match the sounds they have recorded. Play a game of Sound Snap with them.

You could also try....

‣ playing some music to a group of children and asking them to draw pictures to represent what they hear. Provide a variety of pencils and pens in different colours for this activity. Try contrasting moods and styles of music.
‣ drawing sound 'pictures' or patterns of the indoor and outdoor environment.
‣ using your tape recording to make an interactive display with photos and children's drawings.

Songs, rhymes, stories

‣ Oranges and lemons
‣ I Hear Thunder, I Hear Thunder
‣ We Can Play on the Big Bass Drum
‣ Simon Says
‣ How Green You Are
‣ Peace at Last

Please May I Go to the Toilet?

Focus: Excretion

Context: Excretion is a vital final stage of the combined processes of digestion and respiration. This activity helps children to begin to make a connection between the food they eat and the waste products they eliminate as urine and faeces when they go to the toilet. It provides a good opportunity to stress the importance and normality of these life processes and to emphasise the importance of good personal hygiene.

Just a reminder:

Excretion (getting rid of waste products) is a process common to all living things, plants as well as animals. When animals eat food they break it down to release energy but then need to get rid of the unwanted or indigestible parts of the food in order to stay healthy. This happens at the end of the process of digestion when waste material collects at the end of the large intestine and is excreted as faeces. Toxic waste products produced in the cells of the body are converted into a chemical called urea and pass out of the body as urine.

Look out for:

* Washing our hands carefully every time we have been to the toilet helps to keep us healthy and free from disease.
* Demonstrate to the children how to do this properly and build in regular hand washing as part of your everyday routine.

Key words

* food
* eat
* waste
* toilet
* hands
* wash
* soap
* water
* healthy
* clean
* pet
* animal

The Little Book of Living Things

What you need

* picture books on keeping pets of different types
* pictures and posters about the importance of hand washing
* creatures that the children are looking after in the setting for a short time- eg stick insects, worms, snails or fish

Things to do

* Look at picture books together and talk with the children about the different sorts of pets they may have at home.
* If you have any animals in your setting - for example fish, snails or stick insects, use these as a focus for continuing the discussion.
* Talk about the responsibilities of keeping pets and make a diary of 'A Day in the Life of...'
* Use books and leaflets to find out the different kinds of food pets like to eat, and the importance of providing animals with access to clean drinking water and to clean their cages and habitats.
* Now begin to talk with the children about what happens to food or water that pets' bodies don't need, and how important it is for their pets, and for them, to get rid of this undigested food and excess water.
* Talk about taking dogs out for a walk several times a day, providing a litter tray or cat flap for a cat, and cleaning out hamster, gerbil or rabbit cages.
* Emphasise the importance of the excretion process as a natural part of staying fit and healthy, and talk generally about human toilet habits.
* Look at the toilets in your setting and talk about the importance of keeping the toilets clean and tidy to stop germs from growing. Make sure you give a balanced view of this, don't make children frightened of germs!
* Help the children to make up a set of hand washing rules for the setting, for adults as well as children.

You could also try....

▷ organising a visit from a dog or cat breeder, a veterinary surgeon or pet shop owner, or a representative of the RSPCA.
▷ setting up the role play area as a veterinary surgery or animal sanctuary.
▷ following up your discussion about routines by looking at snack time, washing after visits or playing outside, healthy cooking sessions etc.

Songs, rhymes, stories

▷ I Love Little Pussy, her Coat is so Warm
▷ Ding, Dong Bell, Pussy's in the Well
▷ Who's That Ringing on my Door Bell
▷ This is the Way we Wash our Hands
▷ I want my Potty

Looking After Living Things

This section of the Little Book of Living Things provides some advice on looking after a range of creatures which you might want to keep in your setting for short periods of time. This will give the children an opportunity to observe them more closely and discover a little more about how they feed, move and grow.

The range of living creatures we have included are:

> earthworms
> spiders
> snails
> caterpillars
> stick insects
> frogspawn and tadpoles

Earthworms, spiders and snails are all creatures which you will find in the environment around your setting. They can be kept for a short period in the right conditions and then released back into the wild again, ideally in the same place as you found them.

Caterpillars can be kept for a longer period to watch the changes they go through as they turn into adult butterflies or moths.

Stick insects are not native insects in the United Kingdom, although some have become naturalised in certain parts of the country and can occasionally be found on privet hedges. Stick insects are interesting to keep but should not be released into the wild.

Frogs and toads are protected species in the United Kingdom. If you wish to keep frogspawn to enable children to observe the changes which happen during the frog's life cycle, please follow the instructions on keeping frogspawn carefully. You may want to seek additional advice from your local Wildlife Trust.

Each example on the following pages includes:

    * background information for adults;
    * guidance on how to set up the environment appropriately;
    * ways in which the children can be actively involved;
    * ideas for activities based on the living creatures you are looking after.

Looking After Earthworms

Finding Earthworms

Earthworms are easy to find, simple to catch and fascinating to watch as they move about through the soil creating tunnels and burrows.

What you need

To see the worms easily it is best to keep them in a narrow transparent container so they have to make their burrows close to the surface. You can buy commercially produced wormeries or could try making one yourself using perspex sheet and wood. Alternatively you could set your wormery up in a large transparent container such as a plastic fish bowl or large plastic sweet jar. Make sure the black paper cover fits closely so no light can get in. Some of your earthworms may then make their tunnels close to the edge of the container so the children will be able to see them easily.

If you set your wormery up with lots of different layers in it, each a slightly different colour and texture, the children will be able to see how the earthworms move the different layers of the soil around as they burrow through it and feed.

Setting up a home for Earthworms

The children will be able to help with all the stages of this process, but need to be reminded not to put their fingers in their mouths, and of the importance of washing their hands thoroughly when they are finished.

1. Put a layer of small pebbles in the bottom of the container to act as a drainage layer and stop the whole thing getting too soggy.
2. Cover this with a layer of potting compost.
3. Add the soil containing earthworms that the children have dug up from the garden. You will need about four or five worms for your wormery.
4. Put a layer of fine sandy soil on top.
5. Cover this with another layer of potting compost.
6. Scatter some dead leaves or small pieces of lettuce or cabbage leaf on the surface of the top layer.
7. To mimic their natural conditions you will want to keep the worms in the dark, so cover the outside of the container with a sheet of black paper.
8. Cover the top of the container with black paper, with holes punched in it so the air can circulate.
9. Keep the soil in your wormery damp, but not soaked. Spraying the surface with a garden hand spray works well.

Observing Earthworms

* Make sure the soil in your wormery is kept damp, and remove the black paper when you want to see what the worms have been doing.
* Check the wormery from time to time to see what the worms have done:

    Can you see anything on the surface?

    What has happened to the leaves?

    Can you see anything through the sides of the container?

    What has happened to the different layers of soil?
* Talk to the children about how useful earthworms are for clearing up fallen leaves and plant material and for helping to break up the soil and let the air in to it.
* Older children may like to record some of their observations in photos, drawings or paintings. Provide a camera, some clipboards or white boards and stools or chairs for extended watching.
* You could set up a worm composter to recycle your garden waste or to add some worms to an established compost heap.
* After a few weeks help the children to release the earthworms back in to the garden in the same area that they were collected from. If you put them on the surface of some damp earth they will quickly burrow down underground.

Looking After Spiders

Some children may be frightened of spiders, so looking after a spider is one way of making them more confident. It is important that adults act as good role models when dealing with these creatures. If you don't like spiders make sure that you don't pass a negative attitude on to the children by reacting badly to them!

Finding Spiders

Spiders can only be kept in captivity for short periods of time as they are carnivorous and need to catch insects to survive. The best time to find garden spiders is in autumn, on a bright dewy or frosty morning when their webs are easy to spot.

Spiders usually drop down from their webs when they are disturbed, so if you hold a small jar under the spider, tap the web gently and the spider will drop into the jar.

Cover the jar and transfer the spider straight into your prepared spider tank.

After you have observed the spider for two or three days return it back where it was found.

Setting up a home for Spiders

An ideal spider home can be created in a large plastic fish tank.

1. Make sure there is enough room in your tank for the spider to spin its web.
2. Put a layer of damp soil or compost, or a wad of wet cotton wool, into the container to keep the atmosphere moist for web making.
3. Cover this with a layer of potting compost.
4. Add one or two branching twigs for the spider to climb on.
5. Check that the lid of the tank fits tightly - spiders are good at escaping! Make SMALL holes in the lid for air circulation
6. Place **one** spider in the tank. They don't like competition.
7. Keep the tank out of direct sunlight where the children can observe it easily.
8. Return the spider to their own habitat after a few days. You can always borrow another one for children who become really interested.

Don't forget to read
The Very Busy Spider by Eric Carle.

The Little Book of Living Things

Observing Spiders

* The first thing that the children will be able to observe is the way in which the spider moves. Encourage them to look carefully at the number of legs the spider has, the shape of the body, the direction and speed with which it moves.

* If you are lucky your spider may start to make a web, and the children may be able to watch the spider spinning it. Draw their attention to the way the spider fixes the web to the branches and twigs. Look together at the way the spider's feet stick to the web and the other surfaces in the tank.

* Talk about the shape of the web and what it is for.

* Some of the children may like to draw webs. Using silver or gold fine felt pens on black paper or card is very effective, or you could drizzle lines of glue and sprinkle them with glitter. Children could also use plastic netting to weave webs of natural materials such as straw, twigs and raffia, adding wool, ribbons, strips of paper, beads, feathers and sequins.

* Go on a spider hunt around your setting after a heavy dew, in fog or on a frosty morning. Look in hedges or bushes, under windowsills or in holes in walls and fences.

* You may find some baby spiders to observe. Children will be fascinated with the way these tiny babies can travel long distances to find a new home. When a spiderling leaves the web of its parent it climbs to the top of a bush or blade of grass and spins a long thread of silk which is carried into the open air by the slightest breeze. The breeze lifts the spiderling up and carries it on its thread of gossamer. Ballooning spiders have landed on ships several hundred miles out to sea and on aeroplanes flying high in the air. Make up stories with the children about spiderlings and their travels and adventures.

The Little Book of Living Things

Looking After Snails

Finding Snails

Snails are easy to catch and easy for the children to observe because they move slowly. Different species of snail have interesting and attractive shells. They spiral in different directions, clockwise or anticlockwise, and sometimes have bands or stripes on them. The best places to look for snails are in your log pile, under stones and in piles of leaves.

You may also find them eating the vegetables in your garden. Snails can climb and can be found on walls and fences, particularly if there are plants growing up against them. The best time to find snails is in damp weather or in the early morning after rain or heavy dew.

Setting up a home for Snails

1. Find a large plastic fish tank or a tall plastic sweet jar.
2. Make sure it has a tight fitting lid with small air holes. Snails may move slowly but they don't give up easily, and they are very good at getting through small gaps.
3. Put a layer of damp potting compost or soil in the bottom of the tank.
4. Place some stones and pieces of wood in the tank for the snails to hide under.
5. Add a dish of water or a piece of wet sponge or cotton wool. It is important that the atmosphere in your snail tank stays moist.
6. Provide the snails with some lettuce leaves, pieces of vegetable or oatmeal to eat. Change these regularly to keep the tank pleasant.
7. Put the tank where it can easily be seen but is out of strong sunlight. Snails like shade.

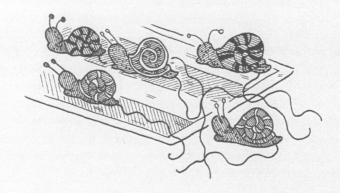

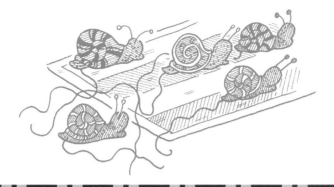

Observing Snails

Make sure the children always wash their hands after handling creatures.

* Give the children hand lenses to observe the snails. Draw their attention to the shape, pattern and colour of the shells, the eyes on tentacles and the head and 'foot' of each snail.
* Try waving a finger gently in front of a snail to see its reaction. Watch the eyes and head!
* Watch them climbing up the side of the tank, where you will be able to see the way they move, and their rasping tongues. You will be able to see the muscles in the foot as they move in waves, and the film of slime that they produce to help them move along.
* Give the snails some cabbage leaves and listen very carefully. What can you hear?
* Organise a Snail Olympics. Put the snails carefully on the edge of a sheet of black card and see which one wins the race to the other end. Does the biggest snail always win the race? Make sure there is a tasty prize for the winner. Look at the trails the snails leave behind them.
* Use this as an opportunity for the children to record their snail's name and their position in the race.
* It is very important to keep your snail tank clean. Snails are voracious eaters and produce lots of waste. Use this as an opportunity to talk to the children about excretion.
* Making clay models of snails provides the opportunity to practise the skills of rolling, flattening and coiling the clay.
* Talk about creatures which have shells and why they have them.
* Sometimes you may find a pile of broken snail shells by a large stone in the garden of your setting. This is a clue that a thrush has been busy!

Looking After Caterpillars

Finding Caterpillars

From late May onwards you may find some caterpillars on the leaves of plants around your setting. Good places to look include nettles and brambles in the wildlife garden area. The most obvious clue to caterpillar activity is lots of leaves with holes in them. Collecting the caterpillars should be done carefully by an adult, ideally wearing soft gloves to protect your hands (and the caterpillars!). Using a paintbrush is a good way of picking up a caterpillar without injuring it.

Take careful note of the plant where you found the caterpillars. This plant will be essential for food, and the caterpillars will die if they don't get the right leaves to eat. Alternatively you may be able to find some butterfly or moth eggs which will then hatch out into caterpillars. Look on the underside of bramble or nettle leaves for these.

Setting up a home for Caterpillars

The _essential_ things to provide are:
* a regular supply of the correct food plant,
* space for the caterpillars to move around in **and**
* somewhere they can pupate safely.

1. A large plastic fish tank with a lid with holes in would be an ideal environment to keep a small number of caterpillars and observe their life cycle.
2. Make sure it has a tight fitting lid.
3. Stand one or more jars of water in the tank to hold the branches of leaves from the caterpillar's food plant.
4. Keep the environment moist using a hand held spray.
5. Provide fresh leaves every day and keep the tank clean by removing any dead leaves.
6. Keep the tank out of the sun in a place where the children can observe it easily.

The Butterfly Life Cycle

* After she has mated with a male butterfly, the adult female lays her eggs on the underside of a plant which will be a good source of food for her babies.
* She then flies away and leaves them to fend for themselves.
* When the eggs hatch small caterpillars emerges and immediately begin feeding on nearby leaves and plants.
* As the caterpillars feed they grow in size, often very quickly.
* When they have reached their full size they shed their skin and turn into a pupa or chrysalis.
* In the wild butterflies may hibernate in this state ready to emerge again when the weather warms up the following Summer.
* Indoors the pupa will remain dormant for a period of time and then the shell of the chrysalis will start to break open and a beautiful butterfly will appear.
* As soon as the wings have hardened the butterfly will fly away, begin feeding and start to look for a mate.

Observing your caterpillars

* Encourage the children to observe the caterpillars daily and see how they change in size.
* Help the children to organise a feeding rota. Whose turn is it to help collect the fresh leaves today?
* Provide hand lenses so they can look closely at their colour, shape, how they feed and how they move.
* Offer fine pens and pencils so children can make drawings of what they can see.
* Ask the children to watch out for the caterpillars pupating. Where do they go when they become a chrysalis?
* Watch out for signs of the new butterflies emerging - make sure they can fly away safely - ideally on a warm, still, sunny day.
* Help the children to re-enact the butterfly life cycle using different types of movement - crawling, chomping, resting, emerging and flying.
* Share the story of the 'Very Hungry Caterpillar' with the children. Encourage them to re-tell the story in movement, pictures or words.

Looking After Stick Insects

Stick Insects

Stick insects are not native to the United Kingdom although some have become naturalised in parts of the country, living in privet hedges.

They are interesting for young children to keep because they are large, fairly slow moving and intriguing in the way they camouflage themselves so they are very difficult to spot in their tank.

What you need

* a large plastic fish tank with a tight fitting lid that has small holes in to allow the air to circulate (muslin can be securely tied over the tank in place of a lid)
* a source of stick insects, or stick insect eggs
* a ready supply of privet to feed your stick insects on
* a hand held spray

Setting up a home for Stick Insects

1. Place some leaf litter (or compost) in the base of the tank.
2. Stand one or more jars of water in the tank to hold the privet twigs.
3. Keep the environment moist using a hand held spray.
4. Provide fresh leaves regularly, and keep the tank clean by removing any dead leaves.
5. Be very careful not to throw the stick insects away when you are cleaning out their tank.
6. Stick insect eggs are small, round and brown and can be hard to distinguish from droppings!
7. Keep the tank out of the sun in a place where the children can observe it easily.

Observing Stick Insects

Make sure the children always wash their hands after handling creatures.

* The children will be fascinated by the way the stick insects blend in with their surroundings. They will need to observe very carefully to spot the insects in the tank.

* Talk to the children about camouflage and the reasons why it is important for many wild creatures. Find a selection of photographs which show animals and their camouflage.

* Stick insects move very slowly and mechanically. The way they move helps them to remain hidden from predators. The children will need to be patient and quiet to observe the stick insects moving.

* Encourage the children to look carefully at the shapes and colours of the stick insects' bodies, legs and gorgeous coloured wings which they flash open at any threat of danger.

* Make a display of words suggested by the children to describe the movement, appearance and texture of the stick insects. Display these with their closely observed drawings, photographs and books.

* Provide a range of resources for the children to choose from to create their own stick insects, and environments for them to inhabit. Try twigs, sticks and leaves or construction sets such as Kid-K'nex, Contruct-o-straws and pipe cleaners.

Looking After Frogspawn & Tadpoles

Finding Frogspawn and Tadpoles

Frogs and toads are protected species in the United Kingdom.
It is important that you collect only a small amount of frogspawn with the permission of the pond owner and that you return the spawn or tadpoles back to where they came from. Ideally, you will collect the frogspawn from your own pond.

Setting up a home for Frogspawn and Tadpoles

Do steps 1 - 5 BEFORE collecting the frogspawn!

1. Use a large plastic tank with a lid.
2. Half fill it with water and let it stand for a day before introducing the frogspawn you have collected. This will give time for the chemicals in tap water to evaporate.
3. Put some large stones into the tank so they rise above the surface of the water. The froglets will drown if they can't get out of the water to rest.
4. It would be ideal to set up a simple aquarium filter to keep the water oxygenated and fresh. Get advice on the best one from an aquarium shop or garden centre.
5. Put some pond weed in to the tank. This could be from the pond where you are getting the frog spawn.

6. Add a small amount of frogspawn to the tank.
7. When the tadpoles first hatch out they will be vegetarian so feed them on rabbit food pellets in small amounts.
8. When the tadpoles have grown their back legs they will have become carnivorous and they will enjoy fish food and hard-boiled egg.
9. Change the water regularly to keep the tadpoles healthy.
10. Keep the tank where it can be seen easily but out of direct sunlight.
11. Release the mature tadpoles or young froglets back into the same environment from which they came.

The Frog Life Cycle

By setting up a tadpole tank and watching the frogspawn change over a few weeks you will be able to observe the **frog life cycle.**
This is how young frogs develop in the wild:

* The embryo (within the frogspawn) is ready to hatch about 2-3 weeks after fertilisation.
* 1 day after hatching, the tadpole absorbs oxygen through its skin, attaches itself to weeds and feeds on the remainder of the yolk.
* 2-3 days after hatching, the tadpole's mouth opens and it starts to use its external gills for breathing. It begins to swim and feeds on the surface of the pond weed.
* 3 weeks after hatching, the tadpole is much bigger and the external gills have disappeared.
* 8-10 weeks after hatching, the tadpole's back legs are well formed and front legs are starting to develop. The tadpole comes up to the surface to breathe and becomes carnivorous.
* 12 weeks after hatching, the tadpole's front legs appear, its tail starts to shorten, and its eyes and mouth are much bigger.
* 16 weeks after hatching, the young frog is ready to leave the water, but it stays on land near the water for some time.

Observing your Frogspawn and Tadpoles

* Encourage the children to look closely at the tadpoles every day.
* Keep a pictorial daily diary of how the tadpoles develop. Use the children's close observational drawings or digital photographs. You could add the children's comments you heard as they observe the tadpoles.
* Each child could make a zig-zag book showing the life cycle of the frog.
* Use the experience of keeping tadpoles to talk about the seven life processes.
* Use life cycle jigsaws and models to encourage conversation about the different stages of development in the frog's life cycle.
* Build on the children's interest by introducing other life cycles such as the butterfly and plants. Use books, photographs and models as starting points for discussion.
* Watching the tadpoles develop will provide a starting point for movement activities, such as hopping, wriggling and crawling. Try singing 'Five Little Speckled Frogs' complete with the actions.

Around Your Setting

Here are some ideas for ways in which you can develop the outdoor area around your setting to make it more attractive to all sorts of different wildlife. Some of the suggestions are very simple and straightforward and will give results in a few weeks. Others require a little more planning and will be longer term projects for you and the children to be involved in over one or more growing seasons.

Before you start, look carefully at your outdoor area as a whole and assess how it is currently being used.

? Are there any areas which are currently under used and are ready for development?

? Are there some barren, exposed areas which need softening, or changing completely?

Everyone's setting will be different and it will be up to you, in consultation with your colleagues and the children, to decide which areas you would like to change and which areas to keep the same. If you would like some advice on this important first stage of the process contact one of the organisations listed in the Appendix who will be happy to help.

Involving the children in making plans for changing your outdoor area to make it more 'living things friendly' will help them to become fully involved in the project and will provide the starting point for many of the activities described in other sections of this book. As the project develops they will be able to see their ideas becoming reality and will begin to understand their responsibility for taking care of other living creatures and their habitats.

Once you have made your plan don't expect to be able to follow it exactly. Things will change   as a result of the weather, or an invasion of garden pests for instance, and you will need to adapt accordingly. Look on these as positive learning opportunities for everyone and as good ways of developing practical problem solving skills, resilience and emotional competence.

Remember, even small changes can make a big difference. Putting up a bird feeder where the children can see it from a window, or leaving some upturned flower pots in a corner of the paved area will encourage birds and woodlice within a matter of a few days or weeks. The real joy in developing your outdoor area in this way lies in the unexpected - not knowing exactly what you might find when you go outside to look carefully every morning.

Creating a wildlife-friendly garden

Designating a corner of your garden as a wildlife area creates a mini-habitat for many native plants and animals - invertebrates and birds and, if you are lucky, perhaps even small mammals. The plants you want to encourage are those which provide food or shelter for different animal species.

Butterflies are attracted by wildflowers which produce lots of nectar for them to feed on, including cowslips, scabious, knapweed, toadflax and clover. To complete their life cycle they also need somewhere to lay their eggs and for caterpillars to feed on. Nettles provide an ideal food plant for the caterpillars of many butterflies including the red admiral, small tortoiseshell and peacock. You can often find their eggs on the underside of the leaves. Teasels produce lots of seeds which are particularly attractive to chaffinches, as well as being interesting to examine closely.

> Nettles are very invasive and can cause skin irritation if touched. To contain their spread try planting a small piece of nettle root in a medium sized pot and burying this up to the rim in the soil. With a little planning you can then keep your small nettle patch at the back of your wildlife garden safely out of the reach of the children. You may like to adopt the same policy with brambles, another great food plant for small creatures. Make sure to have dock plants growing next to a nettle patch, as rubbing a dock leaf onto a nettle sting usually works well.

Children can be involved in establishing the wildlife garden by planning where the different plants will go, and then planting out and watering the new plants until they are well established.

Daily visits to the wild life garden will provide opportunities for children to observe change over time as well as finding and identifying a range of small creatures. Some of these could be collected to keep in your setting for a short time so children can observe them more closely.

Wildflower meadow

If you have a piece of spare ground in your outdoor area you could consider planting a meadow area with a mixture of wild flowers and grasses. Only cut the meadow in the autumn when the plants have finished flowering and seeding.

You can buy packets of ready selected meadow seeds or you can buy separately meadow buttercups, poppies, ox-eye daisies, cornflowers, birds-foot trefoil and yorkshire fog, crested dogs tail and false oat grasses.

Planting Flowers to Attract Flying Insects

Scented flowers which produce lots of nectar will attract a wide range of bees, butterflies and other flying insects.
You could help the children to grow these from seed or obtain small plants from keen gardeners in your local community.

Good plants to try include:

| aubretia | red valerian | lavender | scabious |
| buddleia | ox eye daisies | heather | sweet peas |

Flower beds or containers should be accessible to the children so they can reach easily to do the planting, weeding and watering.

Other things to think about include:
* providing child sized tools for children
* storage and accessibility of tools
* providing a nearby water supply - ideally a closed water butt connected to one of your drainpipes.
* supervision of children while they are handling tools.

You may decide to establish a sensory garden in one area of your setting to encourage children to use their all their senses;

Good plants for a sensory area include:

mint	thyme	sage
lavender	honesty	curry plant
marigolds	pinks	quaking grass
sedum	teasels	hairy grasses

plants with textured or coloured leaves
flowers with strong perfumes

More ideas in The Little Book of Growing Things

The Little Book of Living Things

Building a Compost Heap

A compost heap will give the children a practical example of recycling as well as helping to manage the waste from the outdoor area and creating a free supply of organic fertiliser.

What to do:

* You can either make a compost heap or use a ready-made wooden or plastic composting bin.
* Put the compost bin in a shaded area which is accessible but not in the way. You can add leaves, grass cuttings, dead plants, fruit and vegetable waste, eggshells and used teabags.
* The compost heap should be covered to keep it dry. A sheet of plastic will do.
* Air needs to circulate to help the waste to rot, so either get a container with legs, prop the container on bricks, or turn the heap regularly with a garden fork.
* If you want to speed up the composting process, or to make it more exciting for the children, try adding some composting worms. These can be bought commercially and will eat half their own body weight in waste each day!

Warning!

Occasionally slow worms lay their eggs in compost heaps. Slow worms are actually legless lizards and are harmless. Let the children have a brief look, but be careful not to disturb them.

Establishing a Log Pile

The purpose of a log pile is to provide food, shelter and a breeding ground for a wide range of small invertebrates.

*   The ideal starting material will be some wood that has already started to rot, and you could add some fallen leaves and twigs.
*   Keep the pile low so it doesn't present a hazard to children.
*   Discuss with the children where you are going to position your log pile. Somewhere shady and damp where it is not going to be disturbed is ideal. Let the children help to create it.
*   Encourage the children to check the pile regularly to see what they can find.
*   Some creatures can be removed to study more closely, but make sure the children understand the importance of replacing any leaves, wood or bark they have turned over or moved.
*   You could use the log pile as the starting point for drawing attention to the features of different invertebrates you find.

Use the children's investigations of the log pile as a starting point for a discussion.

For example:

> ? Does it have legs?
> ? If the answer is 'No' it could be a worm, a slug or a snail.
> ? If the answer is 'Yes' then ask
> ? 'How many legs does it have?'
> ? If the answer is 'Eight' ask 'Is it a spider?'
> ? If the answer is 'Six' ask 'Is it an insect?'
> ? If the answer is '14' ask 'Is it a woodlouse?'
> ? If the answer is 'Lots' then it could be a millipede or a centipede.

Growing Vegetables

Make sure that your vegetable plot is easily accessible to the children as they dig and tend their plants. It needs to be near a water supply and the compost heap or bin. Don't forget that you may need to put paving or decking next to a vegetable plot to make wet weather digging easier.

At the beginning of the growing season the vegetable plot will need to be dug over by an adult to ensure the best growing conditions. After that, it should be possible for the children to maintain the plot themselves including adding compost, planting, weeding and watering, all with adult supervision.

Container vegetables

Many vegetables can be grow in containers such as tubs, pots, grow bags and even old tyres.

Plants that thrive in containers include:

dwarf fruit trees	runner beans
lettuce	tomatoes
peppers	aubergines
chillies	ornamental cabbages
strawberries	herbs (chives, mint, thyme, parsley etc)
radishes	cucumbers, marrows and courgettes
melons	blueberries

Homes for Wildlife

Bird feeders and bird baths

Providing a variety of bird feeders and bird food will soon attract feathered visitors to your setting. Make sure that you site them near an escape route, such as a wall or tree so that the birds feel safe. Watching the birds will provide endless learning opportunities for the children.

Try to avoid having bird food on the ground as it can attract vermin. Instead, introduce a bird table and hanging feeders to your outdoor area.

* On the bird table put seed mixes, fat, grated cheese and soaked dried fruit.
* Hanging feeders can be filled with sunflower seeds, and unsalted peanuts, and you can also hang up bought fat cakes and balls.
* Blackbirds and thrushes will enjoy apples and pears.
* Planting berry-bearing trees and bushes such as cotoneaster, rowan and holly, in your garden will provide a regular free source of food for the birds.
* Make sure that you provide a fresh supply of water every day for drinking and bathing - use warm water if it is very cold.

Nest boxes for birds, bats and hedgehogs

Nest boxes can be put up at any time of year to allow the birds to become familiar with them, although boxes erected before the end of February are most likely to be used during the breeding season.

You can fix nest boxes to walls, trees or buildings about 3-4 metres above the ground, in positions where the birds will feel safe, have a clear flight path and protection from the weather, including strong sun. It is important never to disturb the birds during the breeding season, especially when there are young in the nest.

In October or November you will need to thoroughly clean out the nest boxes. You can buy, or make, bat boxes, dormouse nests and hedgehog nesting boxes to attract small mammals to your setting.

A Bug Motel

Ladybirds naturally hibernate in hollow stems. You can provide short lengths of bamboo cane tied together to attract ladybirds and other insects looking for protection over winter. Upturned terracotta plant pots and saucers, airbricks, large stones and short lengths of piping will provide homes for snails, woodlice and beetles.

The Little Book of Living Things

Ponds, Bogs and Pools

If you have room you might think about developing a wet area to add variety to the plants in your setting and to attract more interesting animal species.

In the pond

Developing a pond in your outdoor area will introduce a wide range of different **native plants and animals** to your setting. Ponds don't need to be very big, or very deep, to be successful and will provide interest right through the year.

> **Safety** is of paramount importance if you are thinking of introducing a pond. Children will need adult supervision at all times. **Always check the local LEA guidelines to make sure your pond is within safety regulations.** The pond is best sited at the edge of your outdoor area, in a light, sheltered spot and could be within a secure fenced area to ensure that children have access only with adult supervision. A metal grid can be placed over the pond for added safety.

Regular visits to your pond will ensure that the children have many opportunities to become familiar with the:

> **Water Safety Code:**
> ! Look first before touching
> ! Approach living things quietly
> ! Do not remove whole plants from the pond
> ! Always return animals to the pond after observation
> ! Wash your hands before and after handing living things
> ! Keep rubbish and litter out of ponds.

You could contact Learning through Landscapes or your local Wildlife Trust for advice.

Think bog!

Before you start, you may need to consider whether to have a pond or a bog garden which is wet but has fewer safety implications. Bogs can be just as interesting and attractive to flying insects, frogs, toads and other creatures.

Or Think small!

A small pool in a container such a water tank, tub or even a big bucket can support a water lily, some tadpoles and even a fish. This smaller version may be more suitable for your setting and will still give children many experiences of wildlife.

Building a Pond, Pool or Bog

Planning the pond

Involve the children in planning and building the pond, pool or bog area. Let them help you decide where it will be, how big it will be and its shape. Spend time with the children looking at photographs of natural ponds and talking to them about the sorts of plants which grow there and the animals they attract - frogs, toads, newts, snails, dragonflies and water beetles. It is important that the children are aware that they are creating a specialist wetland habitat which must be cared for and respected over a long period of time.

Making the pond

Record the whole building process in photographs, and involve as many of the children as possible at each stage. Use this to look back on the project later in the year and to talk about how things have changed over time.

The children can help to mark out the shape of the pond, either by using a non-toxic spray dye sold for this purpose or by using pegs and string. They can also do some of the digging of the pond, but you will need to recruit a team of strong and persistent diggers if you plan to make a pond of any size! You will also need to consider how you will dispose of the earth which is dug out.

The easiest way to make a pond water tight is to use a butyl or other flexible liner. It is not necessary to create a deep pond, as most of the wildlife activity will be in the shallow water and around the edges. Make sure that you **remove any sharp stones** and **cover the base of the pond with a layer of padding** (newspaper, carpet or sand) to protect the liner. Bury the surplus liner around the edges of the pond, or cover it with paving stones to make a hard standing at the edge.

As you fill the pond with water (preferably from a rain water butt), the liner will settle into the shape of the hole which you have dug. Leave the water to settle for a few days before you begin stocking the pond. One of the easiest ways of introducing small **vertebrates** is to add a bucket of water from a well established pond.

You will need a selection of **native plants** to provide a good fresh water habitat. Try tall plants such as branched bur reed, sweet grass and greater pond sedge. Yellow flag Irises will thrive around the edge of the pond. Add **floating plants** such as amphibious bistort and broad leaved pondweed.

Leave the pond to grow and mature. Once established the plants will grow vigorously and you will need to thin it out annually.

Investigating the pond

Take the children in small groups to visit the pond on a regular basis.
Ask questions such as,

'Can we see any insects flying around?'
*(You might see dragonflies, damsel flies or
mayflies.)*

'What is happening on the surface?'
(Look for water boatmen and pond skaters.)

'What can you see in the water?'
*(Look carefully to find great diving beetles,
caddis fly larvae or fresh water shrimps.)*

'Can you see any creatures attached to the plants?'
(This where you will spot pond snails and dragonfly nymphs.)

To make it easier to look carefully at what lives in your pond use a plastic jug to remove a sample of water and take it indoors. **Pour your sample carefully into a white pond tray** and use a hand-held or stand magnifier to look closely at your finds. **Provide fine pencils** for the children to make close observational drawing of the wildlife they have found.

If you are lucky the pond will become the home for frogs or toads.
You can encourage this by leaving some longer vegetation and grass around the side

of the pond so that your amphibians have somewhere to shelter and hide. Find out more about looking after frogspawn and tadpoles on page 56.

In the Woods

Before you go

Talk with the children about their knowledge of **trees**.

? What do they look like?

? What do they feel like?

? How big are they?

? Are they all the same?

? Do they look the same all year round?

Look at pictures and photographs of trees and notice similarities and differences. Go outside and help the children to experience any trees you have around your setting.

? Are the trees alive? How do we know?

? How long might they have been there?

? Where did they come from?

? Why do we have trees in the street and in the park or in the garden?

Make a note of all the comments the children make during these discussions. This will provide you with some interesting theories which you might like to investigate further, and will throw up some questions which your trip to the wood might answer.

Plan the trip to the woods with the children. Using pictures and photographs talk about the different things you might be able to find there. Old calendars and cards can be a useful source of pictures.

Talk about different features in an environment - plants and animals. This will help children to focus on the things they want to discover when they are on the woodland visit.

> **Talk about the Country Code:**
> Close all gates behind you
> Don't leave any litter
> Keep dogs under control
> Don't damage or remove any trees, plants or animals.

When you are negotiating the groupings for the visit talk about different woodland treasures which you want each group to look out for. These could include fallen leaves; twigs and small branches, nuts or cones pieces of bark, birds' feathers.

Provide the children with small collector's bags to put their treasures in.

Remind the children not to put anything, including their fingers, in their mouths.

The Little Book of Living Things

While you are there

Help the children to **focus on experiencing the woodland with all their senses**.

? What can you see? Is it light or is it dark?

? What can you hear?

? What can you smell?

? How does it make you feel?

Record or note down the comments they make to so you will have a complete record of the visit to discuss when you re-live the experience back in the setting with the children.

Encourage the children to **be 'Tree Detectives'**:

? Do you think all the trees look exactly the same? Are they the same size ?

? What does the bark feel like? What colour is it?

? What shapes are the leaves? What colours are the leaves? Are they all the same?

? Can you see any flowers or cones or seeds on the tree?

? How tall do you think the tree might be? Stand under a tree and look up. What does it look like? What can you see, what can you hear?

Help the children to **look carefully at the leaf litter under the trees.**

? What colour is it? What does it feel like? What does it smell like?

? Can they see any living creatures in it?

Collect some leaf litter to take back to the setting to look at more closely.

? Can you spot anything living in the trees?

(Oaks are the best species to look at. Try looking in any small holes in the trunk of the tree or in areas where the bark is damaged. Look out for insects, ants, small caterpillars, spiders, snails, woodlice, centipedes, larvae and grubs.)

You could **spread a white cloth or large sheet of paper on the ground** underneath a low branch and tap the branch gently with a walking stick. This can cause great excitement as the small invertebrates drop out of the tree and escape!

? Are there any plants or flowers growing under the trees? What do they look like?

? Can you spot any ferns or mosses or fungi?

? Is there any evidence of birds, squirrels, field mice, foxes, rabbits, badgers, moles?

Evidence to look for includes:

o nests or the sound of bird song;

o nuts and cones that have been nibbled;

o patches of bark stripped off by squirrels;

o tracks or paw prints;

o holes in the ground.

Use a camera to take photographs of all the things the children experience and discover on their woodland visit. Note down the words that the children use while they are investigating different areas of the habitat.

The Little Book of Living Things

When you get back

* **Investigate the leaf litter you have collected** from under the trees. Spread the leaf litter on a light coloured surface and use a pair of plastic tweezers or a wooden chop stick to carefully move the material around and look for any small invertebrates. **Use a Perrys pooter** to collect anything you find and transfer it to a small plastic lidded dish, to look at more closely.

   Invertebrates to look out for include:

earwigs	wood ants	spiders	ground beetles
snails	earthworms	woodlice	millipedes
centipedes	shield bugs	ladybirds	caterpillars

* Remember to **return these animals to their leaf litter home** and put the litter in a suitable place in your outdoor area when you have finished this investigation.

* With the children, **look closely at the collections of leaves, twigs etc** that they have made. Talk with the children about the different colours, textures, shapes and arrangement of the leaves. Compare the tops and the undersides of the leaves and look for the veins which help to give the leaf its shape. **Look for leaf skeletons** among your leaf litter and compare these with the intact leaves.

* See **how many different trees the children can identify** using pictures and photographs and reference books. This is a great activity for encouraging children to look closely and describe carefully what they are able to see.

* **If you have collected any seeds**, including acorns, hazelnuts, beechnuts or conifer seeds you can try planting these to grow some new trees. Before you do this make sure you know where you are going to plant the new trees when they have grown and are ready to be transplanted. Remember oaks, beech and conifers will grow into very large trees, so unless you have lots of space, a hazel nut may be a better bet.

* **Plant the seeds** in a mixture of garden soil and compost about 15cm deep. Bury the seeds to a depth of about 1.5 x their size, and keep watered. When the seedlings have sprouted into young trees help the children to transplant them to a suitable site and keep then watered and weed-free until they are well established.

* Gather together the children's recollections of their woodland visit, words as well as pictures to **make a display or book** to share with parents and visitors.

* Organise the role play area into a tree nursery, garden centre or woodland visitor centre.

* You could **extend the children's experience** by revisiting the wood at different times of the year or by visiting a local National Trust or English Heritage site.

The Little Book of Living Things

At the Seaside

Visiting a beach gives young children the opportunity to experience a habitat which contrasts with that immediately around your setting. The range of plants and animals they find there will be new and exciting and it will smell, feel and sound very different.

Before You Go

Talk with the children about their experiences of going to the beach.

Look at pictures, books and photographs with different beach and sea shore features -

* sandy beaches
* rock pools
* harbours
* sand dunes
* cliffs.

Talk about tides and safety at the water's edge.

* Look at photographs of beach warning signs and flags, and talk about the role of beach lifeguards. Further information is available from: www.beachsafety.org.uk.
* You could organise a visit from an education officer from the Royal National Lifeboat Institution (RNLI) beachsafety@rnli.org.uk to talk to the children (and their parents) about how to enjoy a visit to the beach safely.

Ask the children to predict what sorts of plants and animals they might find at the beach and use this as a starting point for looking at pictures and photographs.

Draw their attention to some of the different environments which exist at the beach:

* above the high tide line - always dry.
* in the rock pools - wet or dry depending on the state of the tide
* below the low tide line - always wet.

Talk about the Seashore Code:

> Always leave plants and animals where you find them.
> Replace upturned rocks and seaweed where you found them.
> Don't remove seaweed that is growing on the rocks - it has taken many years to develop.
> Make sure a shell is empty before you take it home - some become homes for hermit crabs once their original owner has died.
> Take your litter home, never leave it on the beach.
> Don't feed the seagulls.

Read   'Lucy and Tom at the Seaside';
       Shirley Hughes; Puffin Books

While you are there

* Help the children to focus on experiencing the beach with all their senses.
  * ? What can you see?
  * ? What can you hear?
  * ? What can you smell?
  * ? What can you feel?
* Record or note down the comments they make so you will have a complete record of the visit to discuss when you re-live the experience back in the setting with the children.
* Take lots of photographs of the beach environment and the different habitats within it - the tide line, the rocks and the rock pools
* Investigate the high tide line. What treasures can you find?
* Encourage the children to look carefully at the different types of seaweed that have been washed up - its colour, shape, texture and smell. Collect some examples to take back to the setting. Include some bladder wrack if possible, it is great fun to pop.
* Look for pieces of driftwood and talk about its shape and colour. Where might it have come from?
* Look for empty shells in different sizes, colours, shapes and textures. Help the children to gather a collection of shells to take back with them.
* Search for smooth stones and pebbles, noticing their different colours and shapes.
* Feel the sand - is it soft or sharp and gritty? Collect some to take back with you.
* Notice any rubbish on the beach, such as plastic bottles or bags. Draw the children's attention to it, but ask them not to touch it. Take a photo, don't collect it!
* Are there any birds on the beach? Do they make a noise? What colour, size and shape are they. Can you see the shape of their beaks, legs or feet?
* Are there any footprints or tracks on the beach   who could have made them?
* Are there any limpets, barnacles or mussels clinging to the rocks. What will happen to them when the tide comes in?
* Investigate some rock pools with the children. Look for:
  * o sea anemones - these are often red or purple and look like small blobs of jelly;
  * o sea urchins - covered in spines
  * o seaweed - delicate green sea lettuce and red encrusting seaweed
  * o molluscs - topshells, whelks and winkles;
  * o hermit crabs - soft bodied crabs which live in discarded mollusc shells;
  * o shrimps - almost transparent and hard to spot;
  * o starfish - five legs and suckers underneath;
  * o crabs - hide under seaweed and rocks;
  * o small fish - rock goby, butterfish and shanny.

Look carefully, take photographs
but don't disturb.

The Little Book of Living Things

When you get back

* Spend some time revisiting the beach experience with the children. Help them to recall all the different things you saw, heard and did.
* Can they remember the smell, sound and sight of the seaside?
* Look at the different treasures - shells, stones and seaweed you collected, and help the children to identify them using pictures and illustrated reference book.
* Examine the sand you brought back, its texture and colour. Look carefully at it with a magnifying glass   what can you see?
* Look at the texture of sea weed in more detail. Encourage the children to think up their own words to describe how it feels, when it is wet and when it is dry.
* Try hanging up a length of seaweed as a seaweed barometer. When the weather is dry the seaweed will be dry and crisp, but when it is going to rain the seaweed will absorb moisture from the air and will become soft.
* Encourage the children to create some seashore patterns or designs using stones, driftwood, sand and shells. Don't use glue - these are meant to be temporary arrangements which can be re arranged into new shapes and patterns by the children.
* Work alongside the children to re-create a sea shore environment in the sand tray or a paint roller tray, or outside in a builders tray. Support one end of the tray so it is slightly higher, put in some sand to form the beach and then pour in water to mimic the sea. Invite the children to add some small world play resources as well as some of the shells, stones and driftwood treasure you brought back.
* Use the photos of any rubbish on the beach as a starting point for a discussion about our responsibility to respect and protect different natural habitats
* Make a photographic record in a book or a display to illustrate your beach visit. Include the words the children used to describe their experiences and discoveries.
* Set out some of the beach treasures, and some magnifying glasses alongside appropriate reference books, and invite older children to be Seashore Detectives and identify their finds.
* Convert the role play area into a lifeguard base or coast guard station. Or help the children to create an imaginary undersea world - provide fabrics which they can use to transform themselves. Add masks, snorkels and flippers, swimming costumes, beach towels etc.
* You could extend the children's experience by organising a visit to a marine aquarium or by holding a fundraising event for the RNLI.

The Little Book of Living Things

Information, Books & Resources

Organisations

English Nature www.english-nature.org.uk
Downloadable leaflets : Amphibians in your garden, Minibeasts in the garden.

Forestry Commission www.forestry.org.uk
Information on forests in your area, tree identification and care.

Invertebrate conservation trust www.buglife.org.uk

Learning through Landscapes
Promote the development and use of outdoor space. 'One stop shop' for any issue relating to the development of outdoor areas.
'Early Years Outdoors' is specifically designed to support Foundation Stage practitioners.
www.ltl.org.uk 01962 846258

National Trust www.nationaltrust.org.uk
Children's section featuring the adventures of Trusty the hedgehog.

Royal National Lifeboat Institution www.beachsafety.org.uk
Beach safety information and warning flag code.

Royal Society for the Protection of Birds (RSPB) www.rspb.org.uk
All you want to know about birds and how to enjoy them.

Wildlife trusts www.wildlifetrusts.org.uk
Contact details for the 47 Wildlife Trusts which exist around the country. An invaluable source of information, help and advice.

Woodland Trust www.woodland-trust.org.uk
Information on identifying and growing trees.

Children's Books

    Alfie's Feet; Shirley Hughes

    Alfie's Clothes; Shirley Hughes

    A New Frog; Pamela Richmond and Heather Collins

    Avocado Baby; John Burningham

    Funnybones; Janet & Allen Ahlberg

    Handa's Surprise; Eileen Browne

    I Want my Potty; Tony Ross

    Little Book of Growing Things, Little Book of Nursery Rhymes,
        Little Book of Playground Games; Featherstone Education

    Lucy and Tom at the Seaside; Shirley Hughes

    Oliver's Fruit Salad; Vivian French

    Oliver's Vegetables; Vivian French

    Peace at Last; Jill Murphy

    Peepo; Janet & Allan Ahlberg

    Sally and the Limpet; Simon James

    Tilda's Seeds; Melanie Éclair

    Titch; Pat Hutchins

    The Baby's Catalogue; Janet & Allen Ahlberg

    The Bad Tempered Ladybird; Eric Carle

    The Berenstein Bear's New Baby; Stan and Jan Berenstein

    The Owl Who was Afraid of the Dark; Jill Tomlinson

    The Very Busy Spider; Eric Carle

    The Very Hungry Caterpillar; Eric Carle

    Where's Spot?; Eric Hill

    A new frog; My First Look at the Life Cycle of Amphibians; Pamela
    Richmond and Heather Collins

    Attracting Wildlife to your garden; Michael Chinery

    Collins Guide to the Seashore

    Collins Guide to the Insects of Britain and Western Europe

    How to make a Wildlife Garden; Chris Barnes

    The Wildlife Trusts' Handbook of Garden Wildlife; Nicholas Hammond

Resources

Photopacks of small creatures, life cycle puzzles - Wildgoose Catalogue
www.getmapping.com

Stick insects, information books, invertebrate homes - Insect Lore
www.insectlore.co.uk

Bird food and feeders, composting systems, native wildflowers and wildlife gardening -
Wiggly wigglers
www.wigglywigglers.co.uk

Plastic tanks, Perry's pooters, pond trays , hand held and stand magnifiers, children's
gardening tools, books and posters - Commotion Group
www.commotiongroup.co.uk

Songs and music - book and CD pack **'Taking Care of Myself'** - Out of the Ark Music
www.outoftheark.com

Kid Knex - Education Essentials
www.educationessentials.co.uk

Construct-o-Straws - Cochranes of Oxford
www.cochranes.co.uk

Collection bags and story boards - Three Bears Playthings
www.threebearsplaythings.co.uk

The Little Book of Living Things

If you have found this book useful you might also like ...

**The Little Book of
Growing Things**
LB22
ISBN 1-904187-68-4

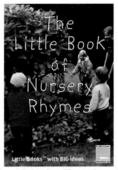

**The Little Book of
Nursery Rhymes**
LB15
ISBN 1-904187-53-6

**The Little Book of
Outdoor Play**
LB3
ISBN 1-902233-74-3

**The Little Book of
Investigations**
LB20
ISBN 1-904187-66-8

All available from

Featherstone Education   PO Box 6350
Lutterworth   LE17 6ZA
T:0185 888 1212   F:0185 888 1360

on our web site

www.featherstone.uk.com

and from selected
book suppliers

The Little Books Club

Little Books meet the need for exciting and practical activities which are fun to do, address the Early Learning Goals and can be followed in most settings. As one user put it

> *"When everything else falls apart I know I can reach for a Little Book and things will be fine!"*

We publish 10 Little Books a year – one a month except for August and December. **Little Books Club members receive each <u>new</u> Little Book on approval at a reduced price** as soon as it is published.

Examine the book at your leisure. Keep it or return it. You decide.

That's all. No strings. No joining fee. No agreement to buy a set number of books during the year. And you can leave at any time.

Little Books Club members receive -

- ♥ *each new Little Book on approval as soon as it's published*
- ♥ *a specially reduced price on that book and on any other Little Books they buy*
- ♥ *a regular, free newsletter dealing with club news and aspects of Early Years curriculum and practice*
- ♥ *free postage on anything ordered from our catalogue*
- ♥ *a discount voucher on joining which can be used to buy from our catalogue*
- ♥ *at least one other special offer every month*

There's always something in Little Books to help and inspire you!

Phone 0185 888 1212 for details